Stewardship

Instruction Manual

By Steven P. Demme

1-888-854-MATH (6284) - MathUSee.com
Sales@MathUSee.com

Sales@MathUSee.com - 1-888-854-MATH (6284) - MathUSee.com

Stewardship

SCOPE AND SEQUENCE

Math·U·See is a complete and comprehensive K-12 math curriculum. While each book focuses on a specific theme, subsequent books continuously review and integrate topics and concepts presented in previous levels.

Early Learners Series

Primer

General Math (Greek Letter) Series

α Alpha | Focus: Single-Digit Addition and Subtraction

β Beta | Focus: Multiple-Digit Addition and Subtraction

γ Gamma | Focus: Multiplication

δ Delta | Focus: Division

ε Epsilon | Focus: Fractions

ζ Zeta | Focus: Decimals and Percents

Secondary Math Series

Pre-Algebra

Algebra 1

Geometry

Algebra 2

PreCalculus with Trigonometry

Calculus

Learning Modules

Stewardship Math | Personal Finance

Visit MathUSee.com for more information about Early Learners, General Math, Secondary Math, and our Learning Modules, along with our other products, including the Skip Count CD and math manipulatives.

HOW TO TEACH STEWARDSHIP

Watch the DVD, read the instruction manual, and do the first two practice pages. To complete the lesson, read the corresponding chapter from the *Biblical Foundations* book. Then complete the final two pages in the student text. These pages review the math topic for that lesson and have questions about the Bible portion. When all of the worksheets have been checked and discussed, take the test for that lesson.

SUPPORT AND RESOURCES

Welcome to the Math·U·See Family!

Math·U·See has a number of resources that can help you in the educational process.

Many of our customer service representatives have been with us for over 10 years. They are able to answer your questions, help you place your student in the appropriate level, and provide knowledgeable support throughout the school year.

We are at most curriculum fairs, where you can meet our team, see the latest products, attend a workshop, meet other Math·U·See users at the booth, and be refreshed. To find the fair nearest you, visit the Events page on our website.

MathUSee.com has many tools to enhance your teaching and provide more practice for your student. You can also find Math·U·See on Facebook and Twitter.

Math·U·See Blog

Interesting insights and up-to-date information appear regularly on the Math·U·See blog. Visit us and get the latest scoop on what is happening.

Newsletter

For news and practical teaching tips, sign up online for the free Math·U·See e-mail newsletter.

Support

There are a variety of helpful tools on our website, including correction lists, assessment tests, answers to questions, and support options. If you have watched the DVD and read the instruction manual and still have a question, you may call us or click the support link. Our trained staff are available to answer a question or walk you through a specific lesson.

Earning Money

Money is what we use to conduct commerce. I am not going to get into the whole idea of money, and whether we need to go back to the gold standard. I am simply stating that money, currency, or dollars and cents is what we use to function in the matter of working, buying, and selling. Generally, the more valuable our work, the more money we make. My first paying job was shoveling snow off driveways for a few dollars. The longer the driveway, the more I charged. I then moved on to grass cutting and received $3.00 at one yard and $4.00 at another. I even had a paper route, but that was a lot of walking and had to be done every day. Plus, I didn't like dogs, or rather they didn't like me. So that job only lasted a few weeks. None of those jobs required any special training, and as a result I received low compensation.

When I turned 16, I worked as a busboy, then a stock boy, and finally a carpenter's helper, all of which paid minimum wage. The minimum wage is set by the government as a standard for paying workers over 16. That year I got between $1.40 and $1.60 per hour for each of these jobs.

Then at the end of the summer of working as a carpenter's helper, I was asked to paint the back gutter of a two-story house. It required being on a ladder three stories up. First I stripped the gutter, then primed it and finally painted it. I worked for five hours and went inside to be paid. The man asked me what I thought it was worth, and after some quick thought I took a deep breath and mentioned $15.00, which was double what I had been getting paid. He quickly wrote out a check for $20.00. When I told my dad about it, he said it was hard to find painters willing to be on a ladder, and that what I had done was specialized work. But that wasn't the end of the story. The next-door neighbors who had seen me painting the gutter asked me to do the high trim on their home. I worked eight hours and charged $32.00. Receiving $4.00 per hour, I felt rich! But more importantly, I was learning a lesson in economics about the relationship between money and the value of labor.

HOURLY PAY

All of the jobs I had when I was in high school were remunerated by the hour. If I worked 10 hours, I was paid for 10 hours. When I worked full time during the summer, I received a weekly paycheck based on how many hours I was on the job. Usually this was 40 hours, but if it rained it may have been 32 hours.

If you work by the hour and want to figure your salary for a year and not just a week, I have found a quick way to estimate it. Take your hourly wage, double it, then add three zeros to the end. If you work for $4.00 per hour, doubling it makes $8.00 and adding three zeros makes $8,000.00. Here is why it works: Generally, an average work week is 40 hours. That is five days per week and eight hours a day. Since you usually work 50 weeks, 40 hours times 50 weeks is 2,000 hours. So $4.00 times 2,000 hours is $8,000.00. The 4 is doubled (x2), and multiplying by 1,000 is the same as adding three zeros.

OVERTIME PAY

A normal work week is 40 hours. If you work more than that, it is called overtime and your pay is computed differently. These numbers will vary, but generally it is 1.5, or one and a half, times a normal hourly wage. If you receive $9.00 per hour and work overtime, you would get $13.50 per hour for the hours beyond 40. If Raleigh is paid $9.00 per hour and worked 46 hours last week, he gets 40 x $9.00 for the normal weekly salary plus 6 x $13.50 for overtime, or $360.00 + $81.00 = $441.00.

If you work on a holiday you get "holiday pay," which is double your normal pay. If Raleigh worked 40 hours, plus nine hours on a holiday, he would receive 40 x $9.00 + 9 x $18.00, or $360.00 + $162.00 = $522.00.

PIECEMEAL

Another way to earn money is what is referred to as piecemeal, per piece, or by the job. When you assemble block sets for me, I pay you by the piece. The faster you work, the more you make. My grandfather used to say you work by the (read slowly) hour . . . after . . . hour . . . after . . . hour, or (read quickly) the jobbity-job-job. If you were paid by the hour, you would not get nearly as many blocks sets assembled as you would if paid by the piece—am I correct? It is human nature.

All of my early work experiences — mowing lawns and shoveling snow — were paid by the job. Delivering papers was by the paper, or by the piece. There are many jobs today that still operate this way and pay piecemeal. Those who hang drywall are often paid by the number of sheets hung on a job. Some delivery companies reimburse their workers by how many packages they pick up and/or deliver.

COMMISSIONS

Then there is a salesman's wage, or commission. Salesmen are paid by how much they sell. The more they sell, the more they earn. A commission is a percentage of the total sale. Real estate salesmen are often paid a flat 3% commission for their work in helping someone sell or purchase a house. If they help sell a house that costs $53,000.00, their commission is $53,000.00 times 3% (.03), or $1,590.00. They may sell one house per day in a good week. The flip side is that they may sell only one house a month during a rough stretch. Making a bunch in one week and then very little for a few weeks is called "feast or famine." Salesmen who work on a pure commission basis work harder than most, since their livelihood depends on their sales. An encyclopedia salesman might receive a 15% sales commission. On a set that runs $1,200.00, this comes to a check for $180.00. If he sells one per night, then sales are good, but if he sells one per week, then he is hungry. Often companies have a base salary for salesmen with a commission added on. This way they are not totally dependent on selling but still retain the incentive, since the more they sell, the more they make.

STEWARDSHIP

LESSON 2

Percent

We'll begin this lesson with a review of what a percent is, and then study how to find a percent. We can change a fraction to a decimal by placing a tenth overlay on top of it. We can go a step further and place the other tenth overlay on top of the first one at a 90 degree angle. See figure 1. Here we change $\frac{2}{5}$ to $\frac{4}{10}$ to $\frac{40}{100}$. Notice that $\frac{4}{10} = .4$ and $\frac{40}{100} = .40$.

Figure 1

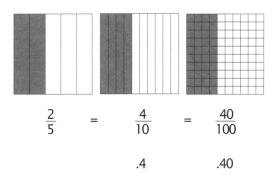

$$\frac{2}{5} \quad = \quad \frac{4}{10} \quad = \quad \frac{40}{100}$$

$$.4 \qquad\qquad .40$$

In figure 2 we take the $\frac{40}{100}$ and show how that fraction is transformed to a percent by taking the one and the two zeros from the number 100 in the denominator and changing them into a percent sign. Now we see how to transform a fraction ($\frac{2}{5}$) to a decimal (.4) to a percent (40%).

Figure 2

$$\frac{40}{100} \quad \frac{40/}{00} \quad \frac{40\!\!\!/}{0} \quad \underline{40\%} \quad 40\%$$

Percent means "per hundred." A percent is another way of writing hundredths. If you can change a fraction to hundredths, then you can easily change it to a percent. The converse is also true. If you have a percent, you can immediately restate it in the form of hundredths. To take a percent of a number, simply change it to hundredths and multiply it by the number. See example 1.

Example 1
Find 25% of 36.
25% = .25 and .25 x 36 = 9
So 25% of 36 is 9.

Another way to solve the same problem would be to change 25% to a fraction, then reduce it and multiply to find a fraction of a number. See example 2.

Example 2
Find 25% of 36.

$$25\% = \frac{25}{100} = \frac{1}{4} \qquad \frac{1}{4} \times 36 = 9$$

Both ways will work. Some problems are easier to work with fractions and others are easier with decimals.

One of the easiest ways for me to think of percents is in terms of money. One percent means one per hundred, or one penny for each dollar. Three percent of one dollar is three pennies per dollar or three cents. Ten percent of one dollar is 10 pennies per dollar or 10 cents. A common application of percents is finding the tithe, or the tenth. One tenth is the same as $^{10}/_{100}$ or 10%. One tenth means 1 divided by 10. When you divide by 10 you simply move the decimal point over one place to the left, making it smaller by one decimal place.

$\frac{1}{10}$ or 10% of 6.53 is .653.
$\frac{1}{10}$ or 10% of 17.50 is 1.75.

Now once you have mastered 10%, you can use this trick to figure out 20%, or any multiple of 10%. For example, to find 20% of 4.13, first find 10% by moving the decimal point to the left, making it $\frac{1}{10}$ of what it was, so it is smaller. Ten percent of 4.13 is .413. To find 20%, double it, or multiply it by two, which gives us .826. Now we know that 20% is the same as $^{20}/_{100}$, or .20 written as a decimal.

We could have multiplied 4.13 by .20 (or .2) and gotten .826, but I am trying to teach you to do this in your head so you can use this skill in a restaurant!

TIPS

If you tip a waiter in an eating establishment, you need to figure 15%. The 15% is calculated on the amount of the food bill, not the food bill plus the tax. I do this by figuring 10% and then taking half of that for the 5%. Here is an easy example. You get the bill and are ready to leave a tip. The bill is $24.00. So 10% is $2.40, and half of that (5%) is $1.20; $2.40 plus $1.20 is $3.60, and that is the tip. If you want to know how I really do it, I like to round up or down depending on the service. If I got really good service I would leave $4.00. But if it was okay, and maybe not what it could be, then $3.00 might do. I always leave something, because usually the waiters are paid a minimum salary plus their tips, so they need to receive some tip. I have friends who will not leave any tip if the service was really bad, but everyone has to make their own decisions. The standard tip is 15% or 16%. If you eat out for a special occasion with a number of guests, make sure you don't tip twice. Some restaurants automatically figure the tip into the bill when serving a large group. Now you know to check for this.

I have also done a good bit of traveling and plan on taking a lot of one-dollar bills when I do. I tip the parking service if I leave a car at the garage and he helps me take my bags into his van and unload them at the curb. I usually tip $1.00 per bag handled. The same applies for curb-side boarding, where they help unload the car and check your bags without the line inside of the airport.

I also give a tip to my paper delivery carrier. More and more this is becoming standard procedure. It is up to you to find out what is honorable. My paper bill comes to $72.10 each quarter, so I make the tip an even $8.00, which is about 10%, and it seems to please the carrier. At least he delivers my paper where I can see it! ☺

SALES TAX

Another area of percents you run into regularly is sales tax. This tax varies from state to state. When you learn it you will know the real cost of what you are buying. Include sales tax in your calculations, particularly when you are purchasing a large ticket item like a washing machine or a used car. Five percent is pretty easy to figure: just find 10% and cut it in half. So if you are buying a washing machine at \$350.00, take 10%, which is \$35.00, and cut it in half to get \$17.50, and then add the tax on to the original price. So \$350 + \$17.50 is \$367.50, which is the real cost for the washer.

In Pennsylvania we have a 6% sales tax. There are two ways to figure it. The most direct is to multiply the total by .06. Another way is to do it in your head. First find 5% by taking half of 10%. To find the 1% move the decimal of the total amount two places to the left. If the amount you are being charged is \$120.00, 10% is \$12.00, and half of that is \$6.00. One percent of \$120.00 is \$1.20, so since 6% is 5% plus 1%, then the tax is \$6.00 plus \$1.20, or \$7.20. The direct way is to multiply \$120.00 by six and then move the decimal point two places to the left for \$7.20. Either way will work.

PAYING BILLS

When you see *1% 10 Net 30 Days* on an invoice (an invoice is a bill for you to pay), it indicates two things. The 1% 10 means that if you pay your bill within 10 days, you can deduct 1% from the total. The 30 means that if you do not opt to make use of this discount, you still have to pay within 30 days. Encouraging people to pay quickly is a positive thing for both those paying the invoice and those being paid. If you as the consumer could pay 1% less on items you purchase, it would mean significant savings over a year. To the business offering the discount, cash flow, or having cash on hand with which to do business, is vital. They may have the best product and lots of sales, but if they aren't being paid in a timely fashion, they can't pay their suppliers and workers, and eventually may have to close up shop.

Many businesses take credit cards for payments for the same reason, and for similar fees. But more on this in another lesson.

LESSON 3

Taxes

Regardless of how you are paid, taxes are a big part of your paycheck. The old saying seems to be true that the only things that are certain are death and taxes. You will need to learn a few new terms in this lesson. We'll begin with gross pay and net pay. Gross pay is what you earn, whether by salary, hourly wage, piecemeal pay, or commission. It is what you begin with, or your income. Net pay, or take home pay, is what you really take home after the government has taken its cut of your income. Tax on your income is called income tax. Let's examine a few of the cuts, or income taxes, so you will understand your paycheck. Employers are those who hire you and pay you for your work. Those who are hired are referred to as employees. Where I live I pay several taxes. But yours may be different, since they vary from country to country, state to state, county to county, and school district to school district.

FEDERAL WITHHOLDING TAX

This tax depends on how much you earn in a year. The more you earn, the greater the percentage of your earnings you pay. This is taken from your paycheck and is usually deposited in a local bank by your employer, and then transferred to the Internal Revenue Service, or IRS. When you get a job, you will be asked to fill out a W-4 form, which determines how many exemptions you have. If you are single, you don't have any extra exemptions. When you are married with a few kids, you can get as many as eight exemptions for a family of five. In the example in figure 1, I will compute the pay check with two exemptions and with eight exemptions so you can see the difference.

STATE TAX

Some states don't have this tax, and the amount varies from state to state. In my state it is also taken from your paycheck by your employer and then sent to the state treasury. For me this is a percentage of the gross pay.

COUNTY TAX

This is one of the smaller taxes, and again it is sent directly to the county treasurer without ever touching your hands. In my county it varies for each local school district. Our school district rate is 1.65%, which is high, since the surrounding districts are 1%.

FICA

This acronym stands for Federal Insurance Contribution Act and is the first of several federally imposed payroll taxes. I call these taxes "double dips" because not only does the government take 6.20% from your paycheck for the Social Security portion, but the employer has to match the "contribution" and pay 6.20% as well. FICA funds both Social Security and Medicare. The rate for the Medicare portion is 1.45%. It, too, is matched by the employer. Both of these taxes, Social Security and Medicare, are part of the money deposited at the local bank by the employer and then sent to the government.

SUI

State Unemployment Insurance (SUI) is put into a fund and then withdrawn by those who have lost their job or are out of work. The employee rate is .09% on all of his or her annual earnings. The employer pays 2.072% on the first $8,000.00 earned. This tax is instituted when there are high unemployment rates, so it varies from year to year.

A PAYCHECK

If you receive a weekly paycheck of $846.15 (gross pay), here is what you would be able to take home in my state.

Figure 1

Tax		8 Exemptions	2 Exemptions
Federal Withholding		21.50	72.01
State	3.07%	25.98	25.98
County	1.65%	13.96	13.96
FICA	6.20%	52.46	52.46
FICA	1.45%	12.27	12.27
SUI	0.09%	.76	.76
Total Employee Taxes		$126.93	$177.44

Your net pay is $719.22 with eight exemptions and $668.71 with only two exemptions.

Don't forget, the employer also has to pay taxes on what you earn. They don't come out of your paycheck, but you may see them referred to as employer expenses. Most of the employer taxes have been mentioned, but here they are spelled out again. The one new tax is FUTA, which stands for Federal Unemployment Tax Act. It is computed on the first $7,000.00 of wages earned. It will appear on your paychecks as an employer expense, not an employee expense, in the beginning of the year, until you have reached the maximum contribution. Eight-tenths of a percent (.008) of $7,000.00 is $56.00.

Figure 2

FUTA	0.8%	6.77	6.77
FICA	6.2%	52.46	52.46
FICA	1.45%	12.27	12.27
SUI	2.072%	17.53	17.53
Total Employer Taxes		$89.03	$89.03

If you earned $846.15 and were self-employed, you would have to contribute a total of another 7.65% for the employer's portion of the FICA— Social Security (6.2%) plus FICA Medicare (1.45%). Think of a self-employed worker as the employer and employee!

Parents and Students

Beginning in student lesson 4.3, I ask the student to interview his or her parents for input on the lesson being studied. I do this for several reasons.

1. Parents have valuable experience and wisdom that their children need to hear. I am hoping that the questions in the lessons will facilitate discussion that will benefit parent and student alike.

2. Most of the lessons where these interview questions are found deal with topics that don't have a black and white, right or wrong answer. In discussing the topics you will see facets of the problem that you probably wouldn't have seen by yourself.

3. Parents have a God-given responsibility to teach and instruct their children. God tells us this wisdom is to be passed on in everyday occurrences. "Repeat them again and again to your children. Talk about them when you are at home and when you are on the road, when you are going to bed and when you are getting up" *Deuteronomy 6:7, NLT.* These starter questions could be the topic of conversation around the dinner table or in the car.

There are also some questions for grandparents. While God's principles are eternal and applicable to all generations, they can be fleshed out differently in different time periods. When you discuss these topics with older people, notice trends from one generation to another. (If you do not have access to your grandparents, perhaps a respected church member or elderly neighbor would help you complete your assignment.)

PRIVATE NOTE FOR THE STUDENT

I hope you have a healthy relationship with your parents. God chose you for them and them for you. He then gave instructions to parents and children. The one command that applies specifically to you is to honor your father and mother. Paul notes in Ephesians 6 that this is the only command with a promise. The promise is that you will live long and that it will go well with you. If your attitude towards your dad and mom is not what it should be, let me encourage you to ask God to turn your heart towards your folks and their hearts towards you. Based on Malachi 4:6 and 1 John 5:14 – 15, I am confident He will do just what you ask. "And He shall turn the heart of the fathers to the children, and the heart of the children to their fathers" *Malachi 4:6, KJV.*

"And this is the confidence that we have in him, that, if we ask any thing according to his will, he heareth us: And if we know that he hear us, whatsoever we ask, we know that we have the petitions that we desired of him." *1 John 5:14–15, KJV.*

Jesus Himself submitted to His parents. "And he went down with them and came to Nazareth and was submissive to them" *Luke 2:51, ESV.*

I am pretty sure He was tempted not to honor them. When we are young we think *we* know a lot, but *He* really did! He is God. But as God in the flesh, He was also successful in fighting the temptation to rebel and as such is uniquely qualified to help you and me do the same. "This High Priest of ours understands our weaknesses, for he faced all of the same testings we do, yet he did not sin" *Hebrews 4:15, NLT.*

So when you ask your parents for their input on the questions in the lessons, do so with a humble attitude and listen with a teachable spirit. God has placed you in your parents' home to learn from and to be discipled by them. Your attitude of honoring them will go a long way in determining whether this will be a positive experience for your family. You don't have to agree with all of their conclusions, but hear them out. They have only your best interests at heart. The following verse in Hebrews was not specifically written for parents and children, but I think it does have application since your parents are your primary disciplers. Note the last phrase in particular. "Obey them that have the rule over you, and submit to them: for they watch in behalf of your souls, as they that shall give account; that they may do this with joy, and not with grief" *Hebrews 13:17, ASV.*

STEWARDSHIP

LESSON 4

Banking

Banks are useful for holding your money, saving your money, facilitating the moving of your money, and borrowing money. Banks do not create money. The board of directors of a bank manages money by offering a variety of services to you and your neighbors. The money that is in a bank comes from people who deposit their funds in the bank.

One thing that has always struck me about a bank is the words associated with it. Notice how often you see words like fidelity (which means faith or faithful), trust, or security. We know that it is tempting to put one's trust in riches instead of in God. I am conscious of this as a Christian. Banks like to be thought of as safe places that you can trust to take good care of your hard-earned money. Ultimately God is our refuge and strength, not the corner bank. That being said, let's examine some of the functions of a bank.

CHECKING

The first function is checking. Checking is where you give the bank your money to hold for you. We'll name your bank, Bank 1. When you write a check, the person or place that receives the check takes it to their bank, that we'll call Bank 2, where it is cashed. That piece of paper, your check, is now turned into green cash. Then Bank 2 contacts Bank 1 and the money is turned over to Bank 2.

This service is a convenience for you and for the person you paid. But it is work for the banks, work that they should be paid for. So how are they paid for their checking services?

When you deposit your money into the bank's hands, they don't just sit on it; they use it to make money. Your next-door neighbor may need to borrow $5,000.00 for a new car. He goes to the bank, and they decide he is worth the risk (lending money always is a risk) with the agreement that he pay it back in, say, 12 months at 8% interest. If he honors the agreement, the bank just made 8% on the $5,000.00, or $400.00. To keep it simple, they are lending out your money and making money with it. So the more money that you deposit or place in the bank, the more they can make. You can make deposits in person, through the mail, or electronically by using your computer. Now the more they profit, the less you should pay, since they are using this money very profitably. This affects your fees.

Each bank has separate fees and structures in place for their checking services. If you put in a little money, say, $100.00, then you will probably pay for your checking privileges. If you deposit a lot, like $2,000.00, then you probably won't have any checking fees and will qualify for free checking. In a best case scenario they will even pay you for holding the money. They do this by paying you a percentage of what is in the bank. Currently I receive a bonus of 2% of the money in my checking account. I moved my checking account to this bank because of this bonus. The bank that used to handle my checking account began charging fees regardless of how much money was in my account. At the new bank, I not only get a 2% return, but free checking services as well.

SAVINGS ACCOUNTS

Some banks used to be called savings and loan banks. When I was a child, my brothers and I all had savings accounts at the local bank. With each account came a little book called a passbook, in which the bank would write the amount in your account. When you made withdrawals, they would subtract the amount. All of this was handwritten in the passbook. From time to time they also recorded the interest earned. This was long before computers, which keep track of everything for us now. Banks provided a place for your money to grow. If you had $100.00 in your account and were to receive 3% each year, or annually, then at the end of one year you had $103.00 in your savings account instead of $100.00. If the money was in a shoe box under your bed, you still had only $100.00. Savings accounts are still a function of most banks. These accounts might be special funds like savings for college, for an emergency, or for a new car. If it is not in your wallet, you have a better chance of not spending it.

LOANS

Another service of the bank is making loans. Smaller amounts, such as those needed for a car or a new kitchen, are usually referred to as loans. Larger amounts that are loaned for the purchase of a home are called mortgages. The key components of a loan are how much you have to pay back, which is determined by the percent of the loan, and the time frame in which to pay it back. These are our concern as the lendees, the ones who are borrowing the money.

But the bank, that is the lender, has other concerns: how you are going to pay it back, and whether you have the means with which to pay it back. So there is quite an interview process, along with an application, to determine your ability to pay back what you are borrowing. This is done to establish what kind of a risk you are, or if you have good credit. For a house, the bank will look over your application carefully, because if you can't make your monthly payments (called defaulting), they can always take your house back (called repossessing) and then resell it to get their money back. They want to make sure the house is worth what you are paying for it.

For a car it is different, because you may drive away and not return, so if you don't make your regular payments, it is hard to track you down. Usually you need some sort of collateral, or something worth the price of the car, that will replace the value of the car if you default on your payments. Remember, the money in the bank is your money, and your neighbor's money, so you want them to be careful when they loan out your earnings.

In some circles, a popular loan is the home equity loan. When you make house payments, you pay the interest and the principal. The principal goes toward paying for the house, and the interest goes to the bank. Equity is the amount of your home that you have actually paid for. When you take out a home equity loan, you are borrowing from your home's equity, or what you have paid for so far.

ATM

A relatively new service provided by the bank is an ATM, which stands for Automated Teller Machine. If you get money from a machine owned by your bank, there are no fees involved. But if you are traveling, there is usually a fee of at least $1.00. If you withdraw $100.00, you will pay a 1% fee.

Checking

Figure 1

```
                              NEIGHBORS BANK                    1556
       Joseph B. Unit         12 Main Street
       369 Decimal Street     Goodtown, PA 15000
       Place Value, PA 01234                       DATE  May 17, 2006
                              12–3456/789

PAY TO THE     Manny Tens                              $  125.00
ORDER OF

One hundred twenty-five and 00/100          DOLLARS

MEMO      downpayment boat              Joseph B. Unit
                                        AUTHORIZED SIGNATURE
 ⑊ 001556⑊    ⑊07893456⑊  08⑊ 987654⑊ 02
```

Let's take a look at several items of note on the check. At the top you will find your name and address and the bank's name and address. The "date" space is in the upper right-hand corner. On the line that begins "Pay to the Order of," you put in the name of the person or institution that you want to receive your money. In the rectangle with the dollar sign in front of it, you write the amount you want to have paid using a decimal number, including cents. Below this, on the longest line, you write out that same amount using words. If you want to remind yourself what the check is for, you have the option of making a note in the "Memo" space. Then make sure you sign the check with your signature. The name on the check and the signature should be for the same person. In the example on the DVD I signed "Steve Knowles," even though "Wise Steward" was in the address. I should have actually signed "Wise Steward."

The numbers below the memo space are written in computer script. While not all checks are the same, on our sample check the number 1556 between some unique lines and dots is the number of the check. It is the same as the number above the date in the upper right-hand corner. The next number is 07893456. This is the bank routing number. Look at the numbers below the the bank's name and address, and you will see the same numbers in a different sequence. The third number is your account number. These numbers help banks recognize and communicate with each other.

On the back of the check, at the top after you have turned it sideways, is a place for the receiver of the check to endorse or sign for a deposit. This is the same name as the one beside "Pay to the Order of." If you have a check made out to you, you have three options: 1) Cash it by signing your name on the back of the check and receive cash in exchange from your bank; 2) Deposit it by simply signing your name. It is also a good idea to include the number of your bank account where the money is to be deposited. Then you will receive a receipt that verifies that the money is now in your account. Option 3) Endorse it to someone you want to give the money to. In that case, you write, "Pay to the order of So & So Jones" and then sign your name to show that you are transferring the check to So & So Jones and it is their money now.

When you write a check, make sure that you record all the information in the Transaction Register. If you have a computer for banking, this is done automatically. But if you don't use a computer, you need to compare what you have written on the check with what is entered in the register. I suggest you do these simultaneously. Don't wait until later to enter this information. You will make mistakes and forget. You should also make an entry in your register when you put more money into your checking account. This is called making a deposit. Another idea for those who aren't doing this on a computer is to use checks with a duplicate copy underneath. That way you have a carbon copy of the exact check you have written. This register is crucial to knowing how much money you have in your account. If you don't know your ongoing balance, you will probably incur fees when you write checks for money that is not there. This is called an overdraft.

Whenever you write a check, you subtract this amount from your balance to show you have less money in your account. When you make a deposit, you are adding to your account, so you add this to your balance. An ATM withdrawal will also be subtracted from your account.

You can't go by what the bank or the bank statement tells you when determining your balance, because they don't know how many checks you have written.

If you write a check to your cousin, for example, and he doesn't cash it for several weeks, it won't show up on the bank's records. But you have committed funds to your cousin by means of that check, and they are gone, as far as you are concerned, and you can't spend them on something else.

Each month you will get a statement from the bank (and/or you may view it online at many banks) that you will want to compare with the records in your register. The first part is usually a summary of your previous balance, a total of the checks that have cleared, a total of your deposits, any fees, then a current balance. Remember, this won't agree with your personal register unless all of the checks you have written have cleared by the time your statement goes out, which is very rare. The statement tells you which checks have been turned in to the bank. They are said to have "cleared" if they are on your statement. You need to go through your register and mark those checks that have cleared. Then there is a list of all the activity in your account listed chronologically. This is usually followed by a list of checks that have been paid by the bank, in numerical order. You may also get the checks themselves or photos of them. You may have noticed that I keep saying "usually" or "generally," because banks do things differently. Their statements don't look the same. The best thing is to take your first statement and your register to the bank and ask them to explain how to reconcile your account and how to read the statement. They are glad to help.

Figure 2

			AD-Automatic Deposit	AP-Automatic Payment	ATM-Teller Machine	DC-Debit Card	T-Tax Deductible	TT-Telephone Transfer		
NUMBER OR CODE	DATE	TRANSACTION DESCRIPTION	PAYMENT AMOUNT		✓	FEE	DEPOSIT AMOUNT	$ BALANCE		
	9-7	Opened Account	$				$ 575 00	575	00
1001	9-10	Newspaper Subscription	25	00				550	00
1002	9-12	Groceries	64	50				485	50
1003	9-15	Filled Gas tank	33	20				452	30
1004	9-12	Missionary Support	50	00				402	30
	9-15	Deposited B-day money					60 00	462	30
1005	9-22	Phone Bill	30	00				432	30
1006	9-24	Water Bill	19	67				412	63

When you know how an account like this operates, it makes everybody's job easier. Figure 2 shows a register for one month with six checks written and two deposits. This account began with a $575.00 initial deposit. Figure 3 on the next page shows a statement for the same period.

Figure 3

ACCOUNT STATEMENT

	Statement Date	09-18-2005
	Beginning Date	08-19-2005
	Previous Balance	$0.00

Date	Transaction	Deposits /Credits	Payments /Debits	Balance	Checks Paid		
					#	Date	Amount
9/07	Deposit	575.00		575.00	1001	9/14	25.00
9/13	Check 1002		64.50	510.50	1002	9/14	64.50
9/14	Check 1001		25.00	485.50	1003	9/16	33.20
9/15	Check 1003		33.20	452.30			
9/15	Deposit	60.00		512.30			

First get your register and put a check mark in the square that shows the check has been cleared (figure 4). Do this for the two deposits as well. Notice that the statement dates are from the 19th through the 18th. So the last two checks would obviously not have cleared. Also, it appears that the person we are sending the missionary support check to either did not receive it or did not get to the bank by the 18th. That is why there is a disparity between the register and the statement. On the back of the statement there is usually a place for you to "reconcile" this disparity (figure 5). First fill in the balance on the statement, then add any deposits made since the statement came out. After you have listed the "outstanding" checks, add them up and subtract them from the balance. This should agree with your personal register as shown in figure 4.

Figure 4

■ AD-Automatic Deposit   ■ AP-Automatic Payment   ■ ATM-Teller Machine   ■ DC-Debit Card   ■ T-Tax Deductible   ■ TT-Telephone Transfer

NUMBER OR CODE	DATE	TRANSACTION DESCRIPTION	PAYMENT AMOUNT	✓	FEE	DEPOSIT AMOUNT	$ BALANCE	
	9-7	Opened Account	$	✓		$ 575 00	575	00
1001	9-10	Newspaper Subscription	25 00	✓			550	00
1002	9-12	Groceries	64 50	✓			485	50
1003	9-15	Filled Gas tank	33 20	✓			452	30
1004	9-12	Missionary Support	50 00				402	30
	9-15	Deposited B-day money		✓		60 00	462	30
1005	9-22	Phone Bill	30 00				432	30
1006	9-24	Water Bill	19 67				412	63

Figure 5

BALANCE THIS STATEMENT		$ 512	30
Add			
Deposits made since this statement			00
SUBTOTAL		$ 512	30
Checks issued but not on the statement			
Number	Amount		
1004	50	00	
1005	30	00	
1006	19	67	
TOTAL OUTSTANDING CHECKS		$ 99	67
Subtract (total out. checks from subtotal)		$ 412	63
CURRENT BALANCE		$ 412	63

One thing I haven't mentioned yet is that I have found mistakes in bank statements. When your check is processed, a flesh and blood person reads the amount on the check and types it in the bottom right-hand corner under your signature. This is in computer numbers similar to what is on your check at the bottom left under the memo line. When you find a mistake when reconciling, compare the amount of the check to what they typed in. It is easy for them to read $100.00 and type in $10.00 since it is missing only one zero, but it is an error of $90.00.

Reconciling your checkbook regularly will help you to keep it accurate. One item I did not mention that is on many check statements is the fee for having the account, or from overdrafts (when you write a check for more than is in your account—oops). I am hoping you won't have any, but if you do, the overdraft should be listed as a debit, or payment, and subtracted. If you accumulate interest on your account, it will be recorded as a credit, or deposit, and added. When in doubt, ask questions!

LESSON 6

Interest

There are two kinds of interest: simple and compound. Simple interest is the amount a bank, or savings and loan, pays on the amount you are originally depositing or starting with, known as your principal. If you put $200.00 in a savings account that agrees to pay you 8% interest per year, or annually, you would receive $16.00 at the end of the year (200 x .08 = 16.00). This is straightforward and simple. You need to leave the principal, $200.00, in the bank for the entire year to get the interest payment. The interest is paid only on the principal. Hence the name "simple interest."

But what if another bank decides to compete and says they will pay the same interest rate, but they will compound your interest quarterly? Which is the better overall rate? When they use the term *compound*, they mean they will pay interest on the principal and on the interest you have earned the first quarter, as well as each successive quarter. Since there are four quarters in a year and the rate is 8% per year, you are going to receive 2% each quarter (8% ÷ 4 quarters = 2%). Let's do a quarter at a time and see how these differ.

Example 1
First Quarter
$200 x .02 = $4.00 interest.
Your investment is $200 (principal) + $4 (interest) = $204.00

Second Quarter
$204 x .02 = $4.08 interest.
$204.00 (new total) + $4.08 (new interest) = $208.08

Third Quarter
$208.08 x .02 = $4.16 interest
$208.08 (new total) + $4.16 (new interest) = $212.24

Fourth Quarter
$212.24 x .02 = $4.24 interest
$212.24 (new total) + $4.24 (new interest) = $216.48

A simple interest of 8% gives you $216.00 at the end of the year. But the same principal compounded four times during the year gives you $216.48. This may not look like much, but you can also compound monthly or weekly, and most banks today will compound daily! This same interest rate compounded monthly would yield $216.60, weekly would yield $216.64, and daily would yield $216.66.

The compound daily interest rate is 8.33%. We can figure this by working backwards. The principal has increased from $200.00 to $216.66. What times $200.00 would yield interest of $16.66? Or, What Percent of $200.00 is $16.66? WP x 200 = $16.66. Dividing both sides by 200, the percent is 8.33. So 8.33% of 200 is $16.66. The compound rate is a third of a percentage point more than the simple interest.

THE COMPOUND INTEREST FORMULA

Now that you have seen how much work is involved in computing compound interest, consider the following formula.

$$FV = P\left(1 + \frac{R}{N}\right)^{Y \cdot N}$$

FV is the final value.
P is principal.
R is the rate of interest.
N is the number of times the money is compounded in a year.
Y is the number of years.

Here is example 1 done using the formula above. Because I did not round when using this formula as I did when figuring the problem previously, the answer is different by a penny.

Example 2

$$FV = P\left(1 + \frac{R}{N}\right)^{Y \cdot N}$$

$$FV = 200\left(1 + \frac{8\%}{4}\right)^{1 \cdot 4}$$

$$FV = 200\left(1 + \frac{.08}{4}\right)^{1 \cdot 4}$$

$$FV = 200(1 + .02)^4$$

$$FV = 200(1.02)^4$$

$$FV = 200(1.08243216)$$

$$FV = 216.486 \text{ or } 216.49$$

We have examined one problem for one year. But to fully appreciate the power of compound interest, we need to examine the same problem over 10 years. To do this I am going to use an investment calculator. There is one on our website at mathusee.com/invest.html. Let's begin with our same numbers for our control group of $200.00 and 8% interest. Figuring $16.00 interest each year for 10 years is 16.00 x 10 = $160.00. When added to $200.00, our principal, this yields $360.00. If this is compounded annually for the same time it would look like the table below and the amount would be $431.78. The difference between $431.78 and $360.00 is $71.78. This table may have slightly different results due to differences in how rounding is done.

Figure 1

Year	New Principal	Interest (8%)	Total Dec 31
Year 1	200.00	16.00	216.00
Year 2	216.00	17.28	233.28
Year 3	233.28	18.66	251.94
Year 4	251.94	20.16	272.10
Year 5	272.10	21.77	293.87
Year 6	293.87	23.50	317.37
Year 7	317.37	25.39	342.76
Year 8	342.76	27.43	370.19
Year 9	370.19	29.61	399.80
Year 10	399.80	31.98	431.78

If you had your money in a simple interest account, you would have to receive an interest rate of 11.59% annually to make the same amount as an 8% investment compounded annually. Check my calculations to see if it is true. Because iinvestment calculators do not round to the nearest cent at each step (as you would when doing the calculations manually), they will often come up with answers slightly different from you manual calulations. From here on in this curriculum, we will show the calculations genereated by the tables from Math-U-See's investment calculator and use them in our solutions. If you do these problems manually, answers up to a couple of cents off of the ones given in the solutions manual are acceptable.

Figure 2

$$200 + 8\% \times 10 - 200 + [200(.08) \times 10] - 200 + 160 = 360$$

200.00, plus what percent of 200 for 10 years, equals 431.78?

$$200 + W\%(200) \times 10 = 431.78$$
$$W\%(200) \times 10 = -200$$
$$W\%(200) \times 10 = 231.78$$
$$\frac{W}{100} \cancel{(200)}^{2} \times 10 = 231.78$$
$$W \times 20 = 231.78$$
$$W = \frac{231.78}{20}$$
$$W = 11.59$$

Investing

Let me encourage you to begin to set aside some of your paycheck on a regular basis to save for the future. As we saw in the previous lesson, the sooner you begin saving, the greater will be the impact of compound interest. The tortoise saves a little regularly over a long period of time, while the hare waits until the last minute then begins to save furiously. As in the fable, the tortoise will win every time. If you don't believe me, play with some loan calculators (you may have one in a money program on your computer) or consult the one on our website at mathusee.com/ invest.html. Change the numbers, and you will see the effects of tortoise investing, deliberate and systematic.

INFLATION

One of the reasons you want to make sure you are getting a healthy return on your investment is inflation. If the price of bread and a gallon of gas was the same today as it was 30 years ago, this would not be a big issue. But prices keep rising, and the percentage at which they rise each year is called the rate of inflation. Prices keep inflating or expanding. If your money doesn't keep growing at the same rate at least, then you are losing ground. For example, consider $100.00 put in a shoe box in 1974. That year the price of gasoline for your car was 50 cents per gallon. That $100.00 would have bought 200 gallons of gas. In 2005, with the price at $2.00 per gallon, that same money would buy 50 gallons. The price of gas has increased or inflated.

Not everything goes up. The prices of computers and other electronic items have decreased over the years, but the price of most items increases from year to year. Economists keep track of the cost of many items and come up with an annual percentage increase, which is called the rate of inflation. I mention this to encourage you not to lose money. If you have your money in a savings account at your local bank with a rate of 2%, and inflation is over 3%, then you are not keeping step.

OPTIONS

There are several places to invest your money. Talk to your parents, investment counselors, and advisors at the bank. Read books, and generally educate yourself on the possibilities. This topic is outside the scope of this course, and many helpful books have been written on this subject. I will give you two resources at the end of this lesson for you to explore. But here are two principles I would like to leave with you before examining a few options:

1. Start now and make it a habit to invest regularly.
2. The greater the risk, the higher the potential yield.

Probably the easiest way to get started is to open a savings account at your local bank and make it a habit to contribute to it regularly when you get a paycheck. You will have trouble getting a good percentage rate, but it is very safe and convenient.

CDS

Another area to look at is buying a CD (certificate of deposit). With a CD you loan your money to a bank for a set time period. This will pay a little better, and you will see that the longer you leave your money with the bank, the higher the yield will be. These are advertised in the newspaper, at your bank, and on the Internet. Notice the language about the percentage yields. Recall the last lesson when we started at 8% and then after compounding for a year it turned out to be 8.33%. The initial rate is the annual rate, and the ending rate is the annual yield, or effective yield.

IRA

Another option is opening an IRA, particularly a Roth IRA. IRA stands for Individual Retirement Account. If you put money into one, you are setting aside funds for retirement. The advantage of a Roth IRA is that you pay taxes on your income, then put it into the account. When you take the money out years later, you don't have to pay taxes on it. A normal IRA is the opposite. You don't pay taxes on the money you invest now, but you do later. In my experience I have not seen tax rates decrease, so I think they will continue to go up. I prefer to pay them now and plan on saving later.

REAL ESTATE

Real estate is so called because it is real and it is your estate. Buying a home will probably be your main investment for your retirement years. In most scenarios, if you own a home for many years and then sell it, it will be worth much more than when you bought it. Many people today are buying land as an investment, since, based on trends over the past several decades, it seeps to be the most reliable place to put their money.

When thinking about the future, which is hard to do when you are young, you might want to consider making sure you have a will or a trust set up so that when you die there will be no doubt about who is to inherit your estate. You will also make sure it goes to the right people and not your Uncle Sam, which happens far too often. I have a revocable living trust, which seemed to be far superior to a will when I explored the options. But check out the pluses and minuses of each and do something! Ask your lawyer about a trust. And recognize that lawyers do not get paid nearly as much if you have a trust as they do if you have a will. So it is in their best interest not to steer you in that direction.

RULE OF 72

Try these next two problems and notice the relationship between the initial investment and the final value of your investment.

Example 1
Find the final value of $820.00 invested for 12 years at the annual interest rate of 6%.

Example 2
Find the final value of $820.00 invested for 6 years at the annual interest rate of 12%.

Do you see the similarity between these two problems? In example 1, the final value is $1,650.00; and in example 2, the value is $1,618.53. Do you see any relationship between the number of years and the interest rate? The initial $820.00, when doubled, is $1,640.00. Both of the answers to examples 1 and 2 are close to $1,640.00. Try two more problems to see if you see another pattern developing between the years and the interest rate.

Example 3
Find the final value of $820.00 invested for 8 years at the annual interest rate of 9%.

Example 4
Find the final value of $820.00 invested for 9 years at the annual interest rate of 8%.

The initial value doubled is $1,640.00, which is really close to the answer for example 3, which is $1633.90, and for example 4, which is $1639.18.

In all of these examples, the interest rate times the number of years is 72. This is called the rule of 72. 6 x 12, 12 x 6, 8 x 9, and 9 x 8 all equal 72. The rule of 72 states that if the interest rate times the number of years is 72, then your investment will double in value. We have seen that it is close but not exact. Knowing this rule will help you get a fairly accurate approximation.

> **Investment Resources:**
> *Sound Mind Investing* by Austin Pryor
> Crown Financial Ministries http://crown.org/

Budgeting

This is a subject that everyone must consider. How much money do you need to earn to care for your living expenses and have some left over for savings, emergencies, and giving? It will never be the same for any two people or any two families, because we are all uniquely designed and thus are all different. We have different priorities, different personalities, different spending habits, and, of course, different incomes. The goal is to identify your needs and make sure you have enough *in-come* to cover your *out-go* with enough left over—or surplus—for savings, emergencies, and giving. Remember the title and object of this book. We want to be faithful stewards of God's resources.

IN-COME

Document your income. As we have seen, with all of the taxes taken from your paycheck, it may be less than you think. If you are on a fixed income, this will be easy to figure out. For several years I was a teacher and received a monthly check. I deposited it on the way home, wrote a tithe check, then set aside money for groceries and our other needs for the month. It was the easiest time budgeting I ever experienced. I was on a fixed income. But if you are self-employed, it is more difficult. I also was once a self-employed painter. In the summer and fall when it was dry, I had more work than I did in the spring when it was raining, or in the winter when it was cold. Unless there was indoor work available, I earned less in those seasons. For that job, I would try to average my income over 12 months and use that as a figure to determine my monthly income. An expression that is often used by those self-employed people whose jobs are seasonal is "feast or famine." You are either well off or broke.

OUT-GO

Identify your needs. Carefully and prayerfully make a distinction between your wants and your needs. Food, clothing, shelter, and transportation are needs. A new computer, more CDs, midnight snacks, and an off-road dirt bike are most likely wants. But this is for you, your spouse, and your God to determine. My biggest advice along this line is to collect data. Consider keeping a note card in your wallet and recording every penny you spend for two months. Whether it is a cash purchase or something bought with a check or a credit card, write it down, and at the end of the day, record it in a notebook or computer finance program. This will provide solid data of your spending and help you to project what you will need. It will also reveal spending habits you may not have noticed before. You may be surprised at the results.

SURPLUS

Set aside money for emergencies and the future. You need money not only for daily expenses but also for unforeseen needs that may arise. Create an envelope, or a new savings account, for these situations. Then forget the money is there. This requires discipline and there are no easy shortcuts. Learn to control your spending, develop the habit of saving, and you will be well on your way to being a faithful, godly provider.

SAVE FOR THE FUTURE

Setting aside money for your future is not the responsibility of the government. It is your responsibility. Develop the habit of setting aside funds when you are just beginning to earn an income and that habit will stay with you through the years. My father set aside $10.00 from every paycheck for investing for his retirement. If that amount were adjusted for inflation, it would probably be $50.00 from every paycheck today. But he diligently stuck to it all of his life. Now that he is gone, my mother is able to live well off what he set aside all those years. And that money could have been spent on other things and legitimate needs. He told me of lean times when he was paying off significant bills at the local pharmacy. When

I entered kindergarten I acquired most of the communicable diseases in one year. Then I took them home to my brothers. There were only two weeks when one of us wasn't sick. But he still stuck to his plan and set aside $10.00 from every paycheck. That money grew and was there when my mom needed it.

SAVE FOR SPECIFIC NEEDS

I am not an enveloper. My wife is. I do not have the makeup conducive to setting up accounts in envelopes and then diligently saving for them over a period of time. My wife had a drawer full of real envelopes, and she would regularly put funds in each one until a specific amount was reached. For example, she might want to save $50.00 to buy a new toaster. She writes "toaster" on the envelope and puts $5.00 or $10.00 in at a time until she gets the money, and then goes out and buys the toaster. This is one approach. My approach is always to spend less than I earn, and that has kept us in the black.

SAVE FOR OTHERS

From your surplus, I hope you have some left over for others. I say I hope, because it is a joy to be able to have a little extra to give to meet the needs of your "neighbor." We don't live for ourselves alone. Our first responsibility is to our family, but we also want to be able to care for others as well.

BUDGET CATEGORIES

Many excellent books have been written on this subject, and I suggest you read one. Anything by Larry Burkett at Crown Ministries I recommend. You can access them online at www.crown.org. In his book *The Financial Planning Organizer,* published in 1991, he has two sections that I want to summarize to show you what is available. The first section is entitled "Divisions of Income." He lists five: tithe, taxes, family needs, debts, and surpluses. And then in another section he gives guidelines for a budget, breaking these categories down into more detail. Using percentages, he suggests some guides for a family budget. These are not only helpful for setting a budget, but if you document your family spending habits (as suggested earlier) and figure out your percentages, it will be helpful in revealing possible problem spending areas. His chart lists the percentages for several different family incomes. I have chosen three to illustrate how helpful these categories and percentages can be in determining where you are spending your money. But unless you track your spending for several months, you will not have a handle on where your money is going and how you can be a faithful steward of the money in your possession.

In figure 1, housing includes utilities, such as heating and electric service. Debts is for repayment of existing debts.

Figure 1

Gross Income	15,000	25,000	40,000
1. Tithe	10%	10%	10%
2. Taxes	8%	17.5%	18%

Net Spendable Income (Gross Income minus God and Caesar)
Percentages below are percentages of spendable income.

	15,000	25,000	40,000
3. Housing *	35%	38%	30%
4. Food *	15%	12%	12%
5. Auto *	15%	15%	12%
6. Insurance	5%	5%	5%
7. Debts	5%	5%	5%
8. Recreation	5%	5%	7%
9. Clothing	5%	5%	5%
10. Savings	5%	5%	5%
11. Med./Dental	5%	5%	4%
12. Misc.	5%	5%	7%
13. Investments	-	-	8%

* Housing, food, and auto should not exceed 65% of spendable income.

LESSON 9

Percents at the Store

Even though we have to change percents to hundredths to use them in an equation, percents are still widely used in everyday commerce. Two words we have to learn first are "wholesale" and "retail." When you purchase an item in a store, you are a retail customer buying at a retail store or retail outlet. Let's pick a product, say a knapsack. And let's say you bought it at Joe's Outdoor World. Joe didn't buy this knapsack from a factory in Mexico and then bring it to Delaware to sell to you. Joe bought it from a middleman who we'll say has a warehouse in North Carolina with thousands of knapsacks and other products. Joe figures he will sell about 25 in August, so he places an order with Mike the middleman (who sells for the factory in North Carolina), who sells them to Joe at $12.00 per knapsack. Joe then sells them for $19.95 each. We'll call it $20.00 to round it up to a whole number. For every knapsack he sells, he makes $7.95 or, rounded, $8.00. This is his profit. $19.95 is the retail price. $12.00 is called the wholesale price.

October comes around and Joe still has three knapsacks on the shelf, and they have been sitting there for two months. He decides to have a sale and marks down the price to $14.95. He still makes a few dollars, but you as the consumer now save $5.00 off the retail price. If he still has one knapsack in November, he may sell it for $12.00 just to break even and not make any money. This is a really good sale. You are purchasing the item at the wholesale price.

Now let's look at the percents involved here. $12.00 (wholesale) is 60% of $20.00, which is the retail price. This is a pretty normal markup for an item such as this in a store. A markup of 30% – 40% is necessary to pay for the rent of the building, salaries, utilities, advertising, etc., that are required to run a business. You are also paying for the service Joe is providing for you in letting you come in, examine the knapsacks, and buy one right in your hometown without driving to Mexico to pick it up! So we all benefit here.

When you are describing either the percent markup or discount, make sure you understand what is a percent of what. I used to sell juggling equipment, and the wholesaler, who carried the equipment and sold it to me, the retailer, always said I made 100% on every item. This sounds a lot better than 30%–40%, does it not? It is semantics, or words, that are being changed. He really sold it to me for 50% of the retail price. I could buy a set of three balls for $4.00 and sell them for $8.00. I say that the profit, $4.00, is half of the retail, or 50%. But this particular wholesaler saw $8.00 as double the $4.00 or a full 100% markup of the wholesale price. I was taking a percentage of the retail (50%), and he was taking a percentage of the wholesale (100%). When you are discussing percentages, make sure you know whether it is a percentage of the retail price or of the wholesale price.

In applying this thinking to the knapsack illustration, I saw the $8.00 profit as 40% of the retail, or I could have said that 8.00 was 66 ⅔% of the wholesale.

40% of the retail or .40 x $20.00 = $8.00

66 ⅔% markup of the wholesale or .666 x $12.00 = $8.00

GROCERY STORES

Grocery stores have much less markup on the average item in the store, because they sell much more and they sell it more often. I need a knapsack only once every few years. But I need eggs, bread, and orange juice every week. I've been told their profit is 4%–5% of the retail cost. If a loaf of bread costs $2.50, then the wholesale price is 4% less than $2.50. 4% times $2.50 is 10¢. So the wholesale price is $2.50 minus 10¢ or $2.40.

Example: Which product makes the most profit in a week, a loaf of bread or a knapsack? To be more specific, Greta's Grocery Store sells 295 loaves of bread, and Joe's Outdoor World sells three knapsacks. The knapsack retails for $19.95 and wholesales for $12.00 for a net profit of $7.95. Three times $7.95 is $23.85. Bread retails for $2.50 and wholesales for $2.40 for a net profit of 10¢. The 295 loaves times 10¢ is $29.50. So Greta's Grocery nets $29.50 versus Joe's Outdoor World's $23.75. The bread wins!

PERCENTS IN COMMISSIONS

I also used to sell World Book encyclopedia and found they had a 20% commission. It was a larger ticket purchase, and for a $500.00 set, I made $100.00 or 20% of $500.00. The juggler promoter would have said I was making 25% of the wholesale price of $400.00. I also found that it took an average of five presentations to sell one set. One difference here is that I didn't need to fill my garage full of sets of encyclopedias and have a lot of money invested in them. I took a sample around and then the company paid me a commission of 20%. World Book is one of those companies that doesn't have middlemen. They produce the books then sell them through their sales force and send them directly to the customer. You can't buy a set of them in a Barnes & Noble.

STEWARDSHIP

Credit Cards

To understand the fees of a credit card, let's examine how one works. Another name we often use in referring to these cards is "plastic." Cash is affectionately called "paper," and credit cards are referred to as plastic, which makes sense, doesn't it? The expression "to buy on credit" used to mean that you purchased something and took it home with you, then paid back the store with regular payments until the debt was paid in full. You were borrowing from the store and paying back as you were able, or with arrangements agreed upon by the store. In lesson 8, I mentioned how we had someone sick in our family one year for 50 of the 52 weeks. During that year, my dad was continually visiting the local pharmacy. He told me it took him several years of making payments of $10.00 per month to pay off the bill accrued during that one year of sickness. The pharmacy was extending credit to my dad. They knew him personally and trusted him to pay the money back. (As an aside, I almost flunked kindergarten that year by being absent for 90 days.)

In the same vein, there are credit cards offered by specific stores. You may have a Sears card, a JC Penney card, a Home Depot card, or any number of cards. When you buy something on credit you are dealing directly with the store by using their card. These stores usually offer a significant percentage off your initial purchase as an incentive for signing up. This is attractive bait, but remember there is always a hook in the bait!

The big credit card companies are Visa, Mastercard, American Express, and Discover. These credit card companies operate as a third party. They pay the store for the item you purchase and then bill you. They are extending credit to you in place of the store where you purchased the item, like the pharmacy my dad made arrangements with. But they have fees for providing this service, some hidden and others not so hidden.

For this illustration, let's say you buy a paintball gun for $100.00 from Wal-Mart with a Visa credit card. When you use this card, Visa immediately pays Wal-Mart and then bills you. You assume that Wal-Mart gets the $100.00, but that is not quite true. There is a fee for this service that varies from company to company, but let's say it is 3% for our example. The credit card company pays Wal-Mart $97.00 at the time of the sale ($100.00 minus 3% of $100.00, or $3.00), then bills you $100.00 in the form of a monthly bill, or credit card statement. Wal-Mart has $97.00 in hand and the Visa credit card company gets their $3.00 fee when you pay your bill. Wal-Mart is willing to pay this fee in order to have the money up front. They are a retailer, not a bill collector. Visa is a money lender and bill collector, but not a retailer.

I understand it is not legal now for a business to offer two prices, but not too long ago, there used to be two prices at some gasoline stations—one for cash and one for credit. This was to make up for this hidden fee. If you paid cash, you got a better price because the gas station didn't have an additional fee of 3%–5%. Credit cards are convenient, no doubt about it, and they make buying much easier. It is generally known that they make it too easy. If you purchase only with cash instead of plastic, you will spend less. It is harder to part with cash than it is to charge an item to your credit card.

UNPAID BALANCE

Have you ever wondered why you get several credit card offers per week? Why are these lending companies so anxious to give you a credit card? I am not an expert on plastic, but that should be a warning sign. I think it is because of the money they make, not only on the 3%–5% hidden fee, but on unpaid balances carried from month to month. That will be the topic for the rest of this lesson. If you have a credit card, as I do, and pay off the balance each month, as I also do, then the rest of this lesson is immaterial. But if you are one of the unfortunate ones who regularly carries an unpaid balance from month to month, read on to learn the real cost of a credit card purchase.

For this example, let's pick a home entertainment system that you just have to own as soon as possible. The cost is $500.00, and you buy it with your credit card and so have committed to pay this amount in monthly installments. We'll assume you have an average credit card interest rate of 18%. Now this is the annual rate. So the monthly rate is 18% ÷ 12 months, or 1.5% per month.

Here are several possible scenarios. The first option is to pay back the loan in 12 months. The payment is $45.84. Here is the full amoritzation schedule showing the monthly payment, the amounts that are applied to the principal and interest payments, and the running balance. The other three options are listed here as totals instead of the complete amortization schedules.

Figure 1

Payment	Monthly Payment	Interest	Principal Paid	Balance
				500.00
1	45.84	7.50	38.34	461.66
2	45.84	6.92	38.92	422.74
3	45.84	6.34	39.50	383.24
4	45.84	5.75	40.09	343.15
5	45.84	5.15	40.69	302.46
6	45.84	4.54	41.30	261.16
7	45.84	3.92	41.92	219.24
8	45.84	3.29	42.55	176.69
9	45.84	2.65	43.19	133.50
10	45.84	2.00	43.84	89.66
11	45.84	1.34	44.50	45.16
12	45.84	0.68	45.16	0.00

Figure 2

Monthly Payment	# of Months	Total Paid (Principal + Interest)
45.84	12	550.08 (Shown above)
24.96	24	599.04
18.08	36	650.88
14.69	48	705.12

This is assuming you aren't using your credit card for any other purchases during this time. One very important thing you have to understand is the grace period. It is described in fine print on your credit card agreement. This describes when you will have to begin making payments on the items you purchase. I called my credit card company to find out how long my grace period was. They informed me it was 20 days. My billing cycle goes from December 12 to January 11. So if I purchase five items during this time and the total amount is $700.00, I have

20 days to pay for them without incurring a finance charge or a late fee. I won't pay any interest on these items as long as they are paid for by January 31, which is 20 days after the billing cycle and within the grace period. But if I do not pay this balance till February 5, then I pay a $35.00 late fee and a finance charge on a balance of $700.00. This charge is computed on the average daily balance. Since my annual interest rate is 17.99%, the monthly rate is 17.99% ÷ 12 months, or about 1.5%. The daily rate is 17.99% divided by 365 days. Since I am five days late I would pay .049% per day.

All of this makes sense. But here is the hidden dagger. If I decide to not pay off my balance and just make the minimum payment (which for me is 2% of $700.00 or $14.00), plus the finance charge for five days, as well as the $35.00 late fee, then I no longer have a grace period. If I carry over a balance from month to month, then I am not only paying interest on the original item(s) that I bought in December, but on every succeeding item as soon as I buy it.

Let's go back to our $500.00 home entertainment system. What if we made payments of $35.00 instead of $45.84 per month, while continuing to use the credit card to purchase more stuff at an average of $25.00 per month? With these numbers it would take us 102 months to pay off our balance. The equation is [(500.00 x .015) + 500.00] - 35.00 + 25.00 to find the first balance of $497.50. Then [(497.50 x .015) + 497.50] - 35.00 + 25.00. Observe figure 3.

Figure 3

Payment	Monthly Payment	Add'l Charges	Interest	Principal Paid	Balance
					500.00
1	35.00	25.00	7.50	2.50	497.50
2	35.00	25.00	7.46	2.54	494.96
3	35.00	25.00	7.42	2.58	492.38
4	35.00	25.00	7.39	2.61	489.77
5	35.00	25.00	7.34	2.66	487.11

After the 102 monthly payments we would have spent a total of $3,560.00—the original purchase of $500.00 for the entertainment system, plus $2,550 for the additional $25.00 per month ($25.00 x 102 months), plus $510.00 for interest. The total amount of interest is $510.00. This is 16.72% of $3,050.00.

In the same problem, if you paid $33.00 per month instead of $35.00, it would take you 276 months to pay it off. If you paid only $32.00 per month, you would never pay off the credit card. Figure 4 is the beginning of a payment schedule that will help you to see what is going on with the $32.00 per month scenario.

Figure 4

Payment	Interest	Add'l Charges	Balance
			500.00
32.00	7.50	25.00	500.50
32.00	7.51	25.00	501.01
32.00	7.52	25.00	501.53
32.00	7.52	25.00	502.05
32.00	7.53	25.00	502.58

In this schedule, paying $32.00 and then adding $25.00 is making a net payment of $7.00, which doesn't even cover the interest of $7.50. You will never pay this bill off at this rate.

It seems to me it is much wiser to save up for a new entertainment system than to have a nine-year headache and increase the cost with additional interest, making the cost a lot more than the $500.00 you paid for it originally.

Beware of credit card checks that also arrive regularly in your mail. These are checks that take money from your credit card company, not your bank. When you use one, you are essentially borrowing money from the credit card company at an exorbitant rate, and there is no grace period with these checks. As soon as you use one, you begin incurring finance charges. The same thing will happen if you use your credit card for a cash advance.

By the way, you can write a letter to Equifax Options, PO Box 740241, Atlanta, GA 30374, to have your name removed from the annoying credit card offers. Give your name, mailing address, Social Security number, and signature. Equifax is one of three major credit reporting agencies, along with Experian and TransUnion. When they receive your request, they will remove your name from the list they provide to the mail spammers, and they will forward your request to the other two agencies.

APR

My annual percentage rate (APR) of 17.99% is a variable rate. That means if the prime interest rate, which is currently 5%, goes up one percentage point to 6%, then my variable interest rate also moves up one point to 18.99%.

SHOPPING

When considering getting a credit card, make sure you are comparing apples to apples. Make a list of annual fees, finance charges, late fees, grace periods, and spending limits. Then make an informed decision. If you do get a credit card, keep a list of what you buy with it and compare it with the monthly statement; don't assume anything. You might consider asking your local bank for a free check transaction register to help keep a careful log of credit card usage.

DEBIT CARD

Another alternative to credit cards is debit cards. When you use a debit card, the money is immediately taken out of your bank checking account. This has the plus of not allowing you to spend beyond your means. But there are drawbacks here as well. Make sure you thoroughly investigate the fine print before using one. An article appeared in the *Lancaster New Era,* page 11, on December 27, 2004, about a local college student who used a debit card. "In one month this fall," the article read, "he used his Visa check card for 10 purchases and 8 withdrawals (ATM machine) totaling less than $250.00. En route, he generated nearly $140.00 in fees . . . and almost all for overdrafts. In one case he was charged $31.00 for an 11-cent overdraft."

There are ways to avoid overdraft fees, but speak to your bank about these since they vary.

The article continued, "Each of his (non-home-bank ATM withdrawals) generated a $1.50 fee, enough to trigger at least one of his overdrafts." "Another [pitfall] is the 'hold' that some merchants place on funds that you don't actually wind up spending. For instance, a gas station might put a 25 dollar or 50 dollar hold on your account the moment you swipe your card, to authorize a purchase before the bottom line is known. Holds should disappear when a transaction clears. But if you're not careful, they too can trigger overdrafts." Another area that tripped him up was the order of payment. "[The bank's] practice . . . is to pay the largest checks or debits first. One day on his recent statement, there were posted five purchases, two withdrawals, two ATM fees — and three 31-dollar overdraft charges. The statement lists each day's postings from smallest to largest and doesn't show a running total. If they had posted them [chronologically] as they were listed, only the last transaction would have triggered an overdraft."

PERKS

Another factor in choosing a credit card is the rebate you receive or the perks for using it. I have a credit card with an airline that I fly frequently. If I use it to purchase $19,200.00 during the normal course of spending money, I receive a free flight. Now that flight is probably only going to cost $400.00 and the cost of having that particular card is $59.00 per annum, or per year. $400 is 2% of $19,200, so I look at it as a 2% rebate. My mom has a card that gives her a 5% rebate on gas and groceries. For the rest of her purchases, it is a 1% rebate. So when choosing, choose wisely and consider the different incentives.

Comparison Shopping

There are three key ideas in this lesson. The first is making sure you are comparing apples to apples, the second is considering all of the factors involved in a purchase, and the third is not trusting your eyes. Let's consider several examples to illustrate these points.

APPLES TO APPLES

Recently we had a water softener installed in our home. Periodically I need to buy salt for the unit. Martin's Appliance installed the water softener, so I buy 50 pound (50#) bags for $5.29 at their store. One day I was at Home Depot and saw what appeared to be the same yellow bag for $4.79. My first thought was to buy the salt there in the future and save 50¢ per bag. But upon closer examination, I noticed the bags weren't the same size. The Home Depot bag, which looked identical to the one at Martin's, was only 40 pounds (or 40#). When deciding between two similar products, I needed to compare apples to apples, or a common unit of measure. I decided to find the price per pound. To do this, I divided the pounds into the price. When I worked it out, Martin's was $5.29 ÷ 50, which is $.1058 or 10.58¢ per pound. Home Depot's 40# bag was $.1198 or 11.98¢ per pound. So Martin's was the better buy, even though it didn't initially appear to be so.

Something else I have learned is that often stores will guarantee the lowest price. There used to be two building supply stores that each claimed to offer the lowest prices. When I went in to one of them one day, I pinned down a salesman and asked him how this could be true. He taught me that even though there are Makita Drills in both stores, they don't have the same kind of Makita drill. Or if they seem to be the same drill, they aren't both the same manufacturer. Once again, when doing comparison shopping, make sure you are comparing the same product, and then work it out so you are comparing the same unit pricing, as in price per pound, per ounce, or per hundred.

One time I was shopping for frozen apple juice and noticed there were two cans of different size. The large can was 12 ounces for 84¢, and the small can was 8 ounces for 48¢. In most cases the larger can is the better buy, but I did the division to make sure. I went with the price per ounce and found the large can was 84 ÷ 12 = 7¢ per ounce, and the small can was 48 ÷ 8 = 6¢ per ounce and therefore the better buy.

OTHER FACTORS

In the first example above there is another factor, and that is the distance to the store. Martin's is only eight miles away, while Home Depot is a 20-mile drive. Since it costs at least 25¢ per mile to operate a car (this will vary, depending on the vehicle and the current cost of gas), the 12 miles' difference makes it $3.00 a trip to buy salt. Even if Home Depot were cheaper, it would not be a better buy because of this factor.

I have relatives who are very thrifty when it comes to smaller items like groceries, and they are big fans of coupons. Once they went to four or five stores to find one that honored their coupons, which only amounted to only pennies per can. On another occasion they bought an item and then drove back and returned it because they found they had a coupon at home for a different brand. My huge question is, "What about the dollars you spent driving around to save the nickels and dimes?"

BUYING CLUBS

You can't assume anything anymore. I have seen buying clubs that package their products in larger quantities and with different boxes that cost more per ounce than buying them in a regular supermarket. Even if it is a larger box and a better buy, with larger quantities of perishable items there is a greater chance of not using all of it and having to throw away some of the product. Sometimes smaller is better.

STEWARDSHIP

The easiest thing to do in a grocery store is find what is called unit pricing. Even though there might be different prices for different sizes, unit pricing will give you the price per ounce or price per 100 count. This makes it very easy to be accurate in your comparisons without having to figure this yourself.

DON'T TRUST YOUR EYES

My first real job was at the Whitehall Dairy Mart. I had just turned 16 and I had to pack ice cream, peel potatoes for french fries, serve deli customers, and sweep the floor at the end of the day. Once when I was waiting tables I had two customers order different sizes of soda pop. The large at that time cost 15¢ and the small cost 10¢, but the large glass looked huge in comparison. The guy who had ordered the small took one look at the large and asked me to take the small drink back and bring him a large one. I took it back on the tray and the cook smiled, picked up a large glass, poured the small into it, added an ice cube, and that was it. The drinks were virtually the same size, but the large glass, also used for milkshakes and ice cream sodas, had a fake glass bottom and gave the impression of being much larger, even though it wasn't. If you are curious, ask how many ounces of liquid you get for each size so you can compare numbers and not be deceived by looks.

When I get drinks in a restaurant I almost always ask for no ice. Ice is filler, and the drinks are usually cold anyway. I get a lot more liquid for my dollar.

Example 1

What if you were purchasing two reams of paper for your printer or copy machine and wanted to find the best buy? First you have to identify what weight you want, usually 20# or 24#. Then there is the brightness factor. If you are using the paper for copying or receiving faxes, you might not need a high-quality type, but if you are printing documents that have to look good and feel good, you would want the heavier, brighter paper. Purchasing isn't always just about price. Other factors have to be considered.

Example 2

I was in Kenya once and noticed a price sheet for using their computers to go online. The price sheet looked like this:

50 shillings 20 minutes
100 shillings 40 minutes
200 shillings 60 minutes

Which is the best buy? There are a couple of ways to solve this problem. If we say price per minute, then the minute is in the denominator (price/minute) and is the divisor.

The chart looks like this with our per-minute unit pricing:

50 shillings 20 minutes 50 ÷ 20 = 2.5 shillings per minute
100 shillings 40 minutes 100 ÷ 40 = 2.5 shillings per minute
200 shillings 60 minutes 200 ÷ 60 = 3.3 shillings per minute

Obviously it is better to buy in lots of 50 or 100 shillings.

If you pay 100 shillings and use your 40 minutes, and then do it again, you have spent 200 shillings for 80 minutes on the Internet.

But if you had paid 200 shillings initially, you would have received only 60 minutes! This must be a mistake, but it shows that you can't assume more minutes means a better rate.

By the way, when I left, they still hadn't changed the signs!

Example 3

One of the strangest experiences I have had in comparing apples to apples was when I was buying sand for a sandbox. I borrowed a pickup truck and went to the local lumber yard where I knew the owners. They weighed the truck then sent me down to get a load of sand.

I was to come back and be weighed again when I had a load of sand. The difference between the weight of the empty truck and the full truck would be the weight of the sand, and I would pay by the pound.

It had just rained the night before and the sand was quite heavy. I mentioned this when I was checking out but was confidently assured that it didn't affect the amount of sand because you could add water without changing the volume of sand.

Do you see the fallacy in their reasoning? I never was able to convince them of their error, and I finally dropped it.

I agree that you can have a five-gallon bucket of sand and still add a lot of water to the bucket and it is still the same amount of sand. But I wasn't paying by volume but by weight, and a five-gallon bucket of sand with water is much heavier than a bucket of sand without water.

Phone Plans

To apply some of the principles we have been learning, let's consider signing up for long-distance phone service for your home or getting a cell phone. One of the most important factors in buying anything is first identifying what it is you need. If you walk into a store and don't have a pretty specific idea of what you are looking for, you are vulnerable to the slick ads and the trained sales force. This is true for car buyers as well as milk and egg buyers, and for everything from large ticket purchases to everyday expenses like groceries. If you walk into a grocery store without a list of what you need, then you will probably spend a lot more on unnecessary items. There is not "one best phone plan." There are always many factors that contribute to making a thoughtful and informed decision. So first define what is necessary. Here are some questions to help you in that process.

1. How many minutes a month do you spend on long-distance phone calls? You should have a record from previous statements. If not, keep a record for a week, or a month. It will provide great data.

2. Which people do you call most frequently? Where do they live, in state or out of state?

3. When do you make most of your long-distance calls? Can you make them in the evening or early morning when rates are lower, or do you have to make them during peak daytime hours?

Once you have answered these questions, here are a few other tips that you need to consider. There are more costs than just the price per minute.

1. Monthly fees: Some plans have them and others do not. They are big if you don't make many calls but can be less significant if you speak for hundreds of minutes per month.

2. Are you billed for full minutes or in six-second increments? In other words, if you speak for one minute and 12 seconds, are you billed for two minutes, or one minute and 12 seconds? If you make multiple short calls, this is a major factor to consider, but if you call a few times a month and talk for an hour each time, this is not a factor.

Example 1

Isaac talks for an average of only 120 minutes per month. He hears about a plan for 4¢ per minute, with a $3.00 monthly fee. Ethan also talks for an average of 120 minutes per month and chooses a plan that charges 5.5¢ per minute, with no monthly fee. Which is the best plan for these two fellows with the same needs?

Isaac will spend .04 x 120 = 4.80 + 3.00 = $7.80.
Ethan's bill is .055 x 120 = $6.60.

Ethan has the better deal. With the monthly fee, Isaac is really paying 7.80 ÷ 120 = .065 or 6.5¢ per minute.

Example 2

Isaac has a friend out of state, and he now talks for an average of 300 minutes per month. He still has the plan for 4¢ per minute, with a $3.00 monthly fee. Ethan increases his phone usage to 300 minutes per month and keeps the plan that charges 5.5¢ per minute, with no monthly fee. How do their plans compare now?

Isaac will spend .04 x 300 = 12.00 + 3.00 = $15.00.
Ethan's bill is .055 x 300 = $16.50.

Now Isaac has the better deal. Even with the monthly fee, Isaac is paying $15.00 \div 300 = .05$ or 5¢ per minute.

I know of people who pay a set fee of $30.00 per month for unlimited calling. For Isaac and Ethan this would be a lousy plan, since they talk only 300 minutes per month. But if all of a sudden their needs change and they have to be on the phone for 1,000 minutes each month, this would be a good deal. Sometimes these plans require you to call after 7:00 p.m. and before 8:00 a.m. If you are calling friends and family and can do so after hours, this plan will work. But if you need to be able to call during the day, this won't be the best plan for you.

The bottom line is that when you are considering a plan, go in knowing what your needs are and then plug the numbers into the respective plans so you can discern which one is the best fit for you.

BREAK-EVEN POINT

There is a way to find the point at which two plans are the same rate. I refer to this as the break-even point. It works well when you are comparing apples to apples but not so well when two plans are dissimilar. In example 2, Isaac's plan is $.04 per minute plus $3.00 and Ethan's is $.055 with no fee. If we set the plans equal to each other, we will find when it is the same cost for a certain number of minutes. (M is minutes.)

Example 3

$$.04M + 3.00 = .055M$$

Multiplying by 1,000
$$1,000(.04M + 3.00 = .055M)$$
$$40M + 3,000 = 55M$$

Subtract 40M from both sides
$$3,000 = 15M$$

Divide both sides by 15
$$200 = M$$

Let's check it by using 200 minutes in both plans.

Isaac $200 \times .04 + 3.00 = 11.00$

Ethan $200 \times .055 = 11.00$

It works. To find the break-even point, make the costs equal to each other. Now we know that for under 200 minutes, it is better to use Ethan's plan, and for over 200 minutes Isaac's plan is the better deal.

CELL PHONE PLANS

Cell phone service is very similar. Make sure you have really done your homework on this one because of the length of the contracts. Most providers require a two-year commitment. If you make any changes to your original contract, then the two-year calendar starts again on the date you make those changes. So, determine whether you are going to be talking for 150, 300, 500, or 1,000 minutes per month. Are you calling during peak daytime hours or will the evening work just as well? If you need daytime minutes, make sure you sign up for enough "anytime minutes." These are necessary for calls during the peak time. If you go over the amount in your plan, you pay a per minute charge, which is higher than your normal rate. For example, you have 250 anytime minutes and you talk for 320 minutes that month. The anytime minutes are part of your monthly fee, but then you have an additional charge of 45¢ (this will vary from plan to plan) and you have to pay 70 minutes times 45¢, or $31.50. Here are several other considerations: Do you regularly call friends with the same phone service? If so, you may be able to talk to them for free. If you are going to be using your cell phone for evening calls, make sure you have a strong signal at your home. Also be sure to consider how much the phone costs.

Don't be swayed by the lower rates for more minutes if you don't really need them. Here is what I have and why I have it. I travel frequently and need a phone while on the road. My wife and college-aged kids do not "need" a cell phone, but I want them to have one for emergencies. So I get the plan that fits my needs, then add two more phones as part of a family plan. The second two phones are very reasonably priced. When we call each other, we can talk for free since we are all with the same company. Unfortunately for my wife and me, we live in the country in a hollow and don't get clear service, and very rarely use the free night and weekend minutes. That means we do require a long-distance provider for our home phones. I have friends who use only cell phones, as they always have a signal at their homes and don't want the additional expense of installing a land line in their homes!

LESSON 13

Best Values

Value is more than price. Value includes customer service and a company that stands behind its product. It is intrinsic, or intangible, and not easily seen. When I was younger, I looked almost exclusively at the price tag when making a purchase. If I needed to buy paint, for example, I knew that I could buy good quality paint at a low price at a large department store. As I have grown older—and I hope wiser—I don't mind spending a little more and buying it at a small paint store because of the information and help I receive from the employees who are specialists. They are a resource not available at the large, impersonal megastores.

The same is true for the local hardware store where I buy many things just to maintain our home. The people working there, in particular Terri and Mike, are a wealth of practical information. When I spend a few bucks more for a product, I am also paying for their knowledge. When I had a bad leak in the basement, I went to the hardware store, and they told me which part I needed and how to fix the problem. It is one thing to buy a gizmo for my well pump and another thing to know how to replace it. That is value. And, if that had been the wrong part, they would have swapped the part and given me the proper one. Or if there had been a defect in the gizmo, they would have replaced it without any hassle. All of this information and customer service add up to great value.

Here is a plug for the local hardware store. When I say I spend a few more dollars for an item, I also save on gasoline by buying locally and not driving to the city for the megastores. When I need to purchase only a few items, I save money and time. Now, if I have a large remodeling job, then I hook up the trailer and make my way to the large lumber yards. But if I make a habit of running to the large stores indiscriminately, pretty soon there may not be a local hardware store to help me when I need it. So when I give my business to a "mom and pop" store in my town, I am investing in my town and the future of the small business owner in my midst.

LIFETIME GUARANTEE

Most automobile mechanics I have known have a Sears Craftsman story. Sears Craftsman tools have a lifetime guarantee. If they break or don't work as expected, they are replaced free of charge. My friend Jim was helping me replace the engine in my Buick when we had a fire in the garage. The handles on his new Craftsman tools melted and were unusable. Since he was helping me, I offered to purchase replacement tools. Instead he went into the local Sears and told them what had happened. They replaced the damaged ones. Now guess where Jim and I continue to buy our tools—Sears! That kind of customer service is above and beyond the call of duty, and it engenders tremendous consumer loyalty.

There is another factor to consider when buying a product with a lifetime guarantee. This may seem confusing at first, but stick with me. I have also seen hand tools that carried a "lifetime guarantee" but that I knew would break the first time they were put to serious use. If I am under a car and using one of these tools and it breaks in the middle of a job, that guarantee isn't very attractive at that particular moment. So even guarantees have their limitations.

WARRANTY

When you make a purchase, consider all of the factors and not just the price on the tag. Consider the warranty from the company that makes the product. If it is faulty, will they replace it in a timely fashion or will you have to wait six months? Then factor in what kind of customer service they have and the ongoing technical support. A warranty is the pledge of the company to stand behind their product or service. Remember to register your product and keep track of your warranty papers.

ELECTRONICS

I have found warranties to be particularly important when buying anything electronic. I have purchased a few computers from a local guy who is happy to make sales but almost impossible to reach for any kind of customer support. I won't do business with him anymore because of this. He isn't there when I need his expertise. On the other hand, I have bought several used computers from Walt down the road because of his knowledge and willingness to support what he sells. When there have been repair issues or questions about the computer, he is there to help me or to replace the product. I have dealt with him for years as a result.

When you are buying a used electronic product in particular, be extra careful to make sure of the warranty and what to do if there is a problem. Because computers and other similar products are so intricate and complex, I suggest the following advice: when in doubt, buy it new. Unless you know the person or company you are buying from, get a new one. There is so much that can go wrong, and you often have no way of knowing until it is too late.

LARGE TICKET ITEMS

Other items to consider when buying electronics and other high-tech equipment are the life of the product and additional warranties. Because improvements and changes are occurring so rapidly in the high-tech arena, you want to hesitate before putting extra money into a warranty. Most new products carry a one- or two-year warranty. Then you have the option of paying to extend the original warranty to three to five years. Since many of these items are outdated in a few years, paying additional cash to extend the existing warranty may be a waste of money. It may be that you will want a new one in two years anyway, as is the case with cell phones today (2005). A warranty is a kind of insurance policy, but you don't want to insure a product that may soon be outdated.

On the other hand, if it is an item that you value and you want to make sure you are covered in case it does break, a warranty may be a wise investment, especially since it is almost impossible to fix electronic products yourself or even find someone that can and will fix them. Today the cost of labor is usually far higher than the cost of the materials to fix something. For example, every year or two we buy a new toaster oven. It is cheaper to buy a new model than to carry the old one to a repair shop where the cost of having it repaired is higher than the replacement cost. This wasn't the case 40 years ago when you had repairmen who fixed small appliances for a fraction of the replacement cost, but that has changed in the U.S.

COMPUTERS

One thing most families in the U.S. will continue to invest in is the a computer. My advice is to ask all the questions you can think of when considering a purchase.

I called a friend of mine who builds computers to get the scoop on some of the numbers and abbreviations associated with the world of computers. Here is what I found out.

The first important question to ask is the speed of the CPU (Central Processing Unit). The CPU determines how fast information is processed. It is the speed of your computer. It has been measured in MHZ and now in GHZ. The greater the number the better.

There are three prefixes used most frequently: kilo, mega, and giga. Kilo is approximately 1,000 (1 thousand), mega is 1,000 times that or 1,000,000 (1 million), and giga is 1,000 times that or 1,000,000,000 (1 billion). These numbers have been rounded from the actual numbers, which are from the binary system. Kilo is 2^{10} or 1,024. Mega is 2^{20} or 1,048,576. Giga is 2^{30} or 1,073,741,824. You will see KB, which means kilobytes; MB, which stands for megabytes; and GB, which stands for gigabytes. MHZ means megahertz, and GHZ means giga-hertz, respectively. Since this book was first written I have learned there is a new term being used, the terabyte for one trillion bytes. It is abbreviated TB, T byte, or T-byte.

When you hear someone say that a computer has 50 megs, then it means it has 50 megabytes. Similarly, a gig usually refers to a gigabyte or 1,073,741,824 bytes.

Hertz are a unit of frequency. One hertz has an interval of one second. When you see 65 HZ, there are 65 flashes per second. You will see this term in descriptions of monitors. If you have a rate of less than 60 HZ, your eye will see the faint flashes or flickers on your computer screen. The higher the rate the better. 75 HZ is a common setting. Today flat screens and LCD (liquid crystal display) monitors are more popular. HZ does not apply to an LCD since they do not have flashes or flickers per second.

Next to the CPU in line of importance is the RAM, for Random Access Memory. This measures how much the computer can do at one time. It affects how many programs you may have running at the same time. Once again, the larger the better. You will see in computer catalogs sizes ranging from 2 GB to 4 GB, or even more.

Another item you must consider is the size of your hard drive, which is where you store your data. It is the memory of the unit. This too used to be measured in MB, but now GB are the standard. Unless you have a lot of music and video files which require large amounts of space, a few dozen GB will take care of most people's needs.

PRINTERS

The last computer I bought new came with a brand-new printer at no charge. After I used it for a while I learned why. The price of the ink jet cartridges was ridiculous. Epson seems to be the leader in marketing their product this way. They can make more profit by selling replacement cartridges than by selling the printer in the first place. Even after changing drivers in their computers, many people will stick with their original printer once they get used to it and then continue to buy replacement cartridges for years to come.

A generation ago, a leading shaving razor manufacturer vowed to put a free razor in every home in America. His thinking was that they would all need replacement blades and he would be there to sell them. It was and is a clever marketing scheme. Two years ago I had had enough of cartridges and bought an inexpensive laser printer that has worked famously. It doesn't have color, but I rarely need color. I have saved money compared to the cost of the replacement cartridges, had less hassle replacing them, and had cleaner, crisper printing.

CONCLUSION

Here are some parting thoughts on buying a computer. For many years I purchased computers at least two to three years old. I got them for a very good price and they served me well. I knew what I needed and they met my needs.

When you buy a used computer, make sure you know who you are buying from and have some sort of warranty in case a problem arises. If you are buying a computer from someone who wants to upgrade, and they have taken good care of their machine, you are probably okay. But if you don't know the individual, you may be buying someone else's problem. Be careful.

On the plus side, consider that most people's needs can be met by a used computer. Word processing software hasn't changed significantly for years. What does change almost monthly is technology surrounding the internet, games, music, and video processing. If these aren't big concerns, then a used computer can be acquired inexpensively and will probably meet your needs just fine.

Automobile—Purchase

If you have decided to purchase a new car, there are three options. The first is paying with cash. The second is financing the car, either through your bank or the dealership itself, and the third is leasing. I will give you some numbers, but the most important things to remember are to compare apples to apples, to learn as much as you can by researching and asking questions, and to pray for wisdom. This is a big decision, and regardless of how easy a salesman may make it sound, it is not a matter to be decided quickly.

DEPRECIATION

The first word you need to become familiar with if you are contemplating a new car purchase is "depreciation," which is the opposite of "appreciation." When you drive a new car off the lot, it drops in value several thousand dollars. Different cars have different rates of depreciation, but all cars will depreciate, or lose value, once they are not "new"! A friend told me once that as soon as you drive a new car off the lot, it is a used car with payments.

Recently, I was talking to another friend whose son had just won a new car in a contest. His new Dodge was worth $35,000.00. When the car arrived he thought he would drive it for a month. He put a few hundred miles on it. Then he decided to sell it back to the dealership. For his one-month-old car, he received $21,500.00! This is a true story. I have found that the best time to buy a car is when it is a few years old, say three or four years.

I just bought a three-year-old vehicle for half the price of a new model. Depreciation is most significant the first three to five years of the life of a vehicle. To illustrate this principle, I went on the Internet and found the values of 2000,

2001, 2002, 2003, 2004, and 2005 Ford Taurus SEL four-door sedans as an example. This has been a popular car in America. I used Kelly Blue Book online to get these figures with the standard equipment that came on each vehicle. There are two other sources I would check, which are listed below, but I stuck with the same features on each car, from the same appraisal service, to be consistent in the comparison. Generally, 12,000–15,000 miles is the average for miles driven per year. Kelly Blue Book provided the numbers listed to the left in figure 1. Do you see the point?

Figure 1

2000	5 Years Old	7,340.00
2001	4 Years Old	9,270.00
2002	3 Years Old	11,105.00
2003	2 Years Old	12,705.00
2004	1 Year Old	15,085.00
2005	New	20,997.00

A vice president of investments at Wells Fargo told me he has clients who are very upset if they lose $5,000.00 in their investment portfolio and yet will go out and buy a new car and lose more than that each year in depreciation. The types of cars his clients are purchasing cost a lot more than a Taurus, so they probably lose twice that much in depreciation.

PAYMENT SCHEDULE

Here is what a payment schedule might look like if you were buying the new 2005 Taurus and had placed $997.00 as a down payment. It is for 48 months (four years) at 7% interest. Notice how the total amount you pay is $22,988.39—principal plus interest. You have now paid almost $23,000.00 for the car, which at the end of the fourth year is now probably worth $9,270.00 according to our chart above. And because the bank or the dealership legally owns the car until it is paid off, they will want you to carry the full amount of insurance to protect their investment.

Figure 2

Car Loan Payment Schedule
for 20,000.00 over 48 months at 7% Interest

Balance	Payment	Principal	Interest	Payment
20,000.00	478.92	362.26	116.66	1
19,637.74	478.92	364.37	114.55	2
19,273.37	478.92	366.50	112.42	3
18,906.87	478.92	368.63	110.29	4
(Skipping ahead 3 Years or 41 payments of 478.92)				
1,888.08	478.92	467.91	11.01	45
1,420.17	478.92	470.64	8.28	46
949.53	478.92	473.39	5.53	47
476.15	478.92	476.15	2.77	48
0				

Total # Payments	48
Total Interest Paid	2,988.39
Total Principal Paid	20,000.00

Since you've already gone through the unit on compound interest, you've seen that it is wiser to save up the money first and collect interest than to pay for the car and pay interest, so consider buying with cash. Let me describe what I think is the best way to acquire a new car. Save the money first and drive a used car for a few more years. Here is how to do it. In the example above, in place of making payments of $478.92 on a loan, put $478.92 into a savings account or money market fund. First you will find out for yourself whether you have enough discipline to make those payments, and second, you will have the cash on hand when you do go to buy a car, which will enable you to negotiate a better price. Then, once you own your car, continue making the same deposits and you will have the money saved. You will have it on hand when you go to purchase your next car when the first one wears out. This is the ideal. Personally, I have never purchased a new car and have been content to drive used cars.

When you're ready to buy your new car, shop around for the best deal. That includes checking the Internet and local dealerships. Consider buying a car in the fall or winter when they are clearing off their lots to get ready for next year's models. When I was looking at the prices for a new GM vehicle, I also found out there is a GM credit card that allows you to get rebates on a GM car or truck. And since I was driving a GM van I could also receive a loyalty credit of $750.00 for sticking with GM. There are many twists, so pray and do your homework.

If you are buying a new car, there are more options available due to the Internet. Here are some websites to check out. These change regularly, so do a search for online car buying and to find dealer invoice prices. Most of these addresses were taken from clarkhoward.com.

Info on autos, boats, trucks
http://www.autopedia.com

Lemon Law
http://www.carlemon.com/

Car values
http://www.edmunds.com/
http://www.kbb.com/
http://nadaguides.com
http://www.consumerreports.org/main/home.jsp

Online car buying
http://www.autotrader.com/
http://www.carsdirect.com/home
http://www.autobytel.com

Online used car buying
http://www.ebaymotors.com

If you are living near any type of public transportation, you are probably better off using the bus or train, an occasional taxi for emergencies, your two feet, and a rental vehicle for weekends or trips. It is definitely not as convenient, but it sure will save a lot of money and upkeep. This is particularly true for those living in large cities, where just parking a vehicle is an expensive undertaking. Don't assume that everyone has to have their own car.

Whether you buy it with cash or finance it, you will make more from selling your old car than from trading it in on a newer model. But if there is a question, give the dealer the make and model of your car and ask them to quote you prices both ways.

In all of these negotiations, remember, YOU are in control. You are the customer. Regardless of the pressure to buy from them, you can always say "no, thank you" and walk out the door. They are professionals who do this for a living, but please don't be intimidated. If you are, take along someone who isn't!

If you are considering financing a car, make sure you check out your local bank and compare their offer with the dealer's! This is an important decision, so get it all in writing. Here are some factors to consider and questions to ask.

Ask for all of the details of the dealer financing plan:

1. Interest rate
2. Down payment
3. Cost of the vehicle (which can change when you are financing it)
4. Insurance requirements (Since you are renting their car until it is paid for, they may require additional coverage.)
5. Length of the loan
6. Rebate details
7. Other requirements that you need to be aware of for their loan
8. Potential changes if you finance it through your local bank!

Then go to the bank and ask the same questions. After doing this you will learn things not mentioned in this lesson that you can apply when you go to a different dealer. Does this sound complicated? It is. So move carefully.

If you are responding to an advertisement concerning trade-ins and special discounts, learn all you can without assuming anything. You really won't know if it is a good deal until you do your homework online and/or talk to some other dealers and see how they compare. I've never bought a new car, but if I did, I would do my homework and have a pretty good idea of what the real cost of the car was before I went shopping.

LEASING

Think of a lease as an extended rental agreement. If you lease a car, you will sign a long-term contract committing to making timely payments for the length of the lease. Please read the fine print of this binding legal agreement. There are many potential extra fees in a lease that vary from company to company. One great asset you have is The Consumer Leasing Act (TCLA), which requires that you have all of the fees and requirements in writing. Keep in mind that you are renting the vehicle. The dealer may charge you for wear and tear on the car or for accumulating too many miles. Know these things before you sign a contract.

There are two types of leases—open end and closed end. Open end will have a balloon payment, or a lump sum, to be paid based on their expectations, mileage, general condition, etc. This payment could offset a lower monthly payment. A closed end lease is a done deal regardless of mileage, etc. But you will have a higher payment as a result!

Forewarned is forearmed. (My feeling is that leases are lousy deals. If you enter into one, do it with your eyes open.) Tax laws sometimes have given advantages to businesses leasing vehicles, but these laws change so often that businesses should consult an accountant when making decisions.

LESSON 15

Automobile—Operation

To count the cost of owning a car, there are two factors to consider: your need and the costs. The first question is, How badly do you need one, or what do you need a car for? In other words, are you using it every day as a part of your job, as by a traveling salesman, or do you think it would just be nice to have a car? If you really need one, then you'll probably lean towards a newer, more reliable model. If you don't really need one, then a good used car will probably suffice. Now that we have determined the need, let's look at the costs involved in operating a car. These expenses will vary between a newer vehicle and an older used car.

Figure 1

	Newer	Used
Insurance	Higher	Lower
Regular Maintenance	Similar	Similar
Repairs	Lower	Higher
Gasoline Mileage	Depends	Depends
Depreciation	Higher	Lower
Fees	Same	Same

INSURANCE

Liability insurance is required by law. In most states you must show proof of insurance coverage to register your vehicle and obtain a title. If you want full coverage, you will be carrying liability plus collision and comprehensive. It is simple: The more you pay, the more coverage you get. As in the lesson on purchasing a car, I am focusing on the Ford Taurus. I have chosen the 2001 model as the used car and the 2005 Taurus as the new car.

Figure 2

	2001	2005
Full coverage	509.00	578.00
Liability Only	260.00	260.00

GASOLINE MILEAGE

You may be surprised to learn that this is not the largest part of the cost of keeping a car on the road, but with the rising cost of fuel, it is becoming a more significant factor. The only way to know how much this will be is to estimate how many miles you will drive in a year and divide it by your miles per gallon (mpg). This will tell you how many gallons of gas you'll use; then you can multiply that number by the price of a gallon of gas to determine the annual cost of gasoline.

Let's examine two cars for a specific example. Car number 1 gets 16 mpg and car number 2 gets 22 mpg. Each is driven 15,000 miles per year.

Example 1
Car #1: For total fuel used: 15,000 ÷ 16 mpg = 937.5 gallons.

If the price of gas is $2.75 per gallon, the cost is 937.5 times $2.75, or $2,578.13 for the year.

The price per mile (for gasoline only) in the 16 mpg car is
$2,578.13 ÷ 15,000 = 17.2¢ per mile.

Example 2
Car #2: For total fuel used: 15,000 ÷ 22 mpg = 682 gallons.

If the price of gas is $2.75 per gallon, the the cost is 682 times $2.75, or $1,875.50 for a year's worth of gasoline.

The price per mile (just for gasoline) is
$1,875.50 ÷ 15,000 = 12.5¢ per mile.

The difference of 6 mpg saves me $702.63 annually, or about $117.11 for every one mpg difference.

REPAIRS

Another factor to think of if you are buying an older used car is what kind of mechanic you have nearby. I have a great mechanic who is also a good friend. As a result, I don't mind owning a 15-year-old Jeep. This car requires a lot more attention than my 2002 vehicle. If I didn't have such a good mechanic, I would lean towards owning newer vehicles.

I tried to get figures on the average cost of repairs for a vehicle according to how old it is but couldn't put my hands (or my cursor) on them. But as everyone who owns a car knows, the cost will vary according to where you live, how much you drive it, how you take care of it, etc. In 2004 my 1990 Jeep cost $776.00 in repairs, while the 2002 vehicle cost $375.00. So we will just make the broad statement that all things being equal, the newer the vehicle, the fewer the repairs.

REGULAR MAINTENANCE

This includes fluids, wiper blades, and other small items, but I am focusing on oil changes. If we figure an oil change every 3,000 miles, then there are five in a year. If the cost is around $30.00 each time, that is an annual cost of $150.00.

DEPRECIATION

To illustrate the principle of depreciation, here is the chart from lesson 14 again. I went on the Internet and found the values of a 2000, 2001, 2002, 2003, 2004, and 2005 Ford Taurus SEL four-door sedans as an example. This has been a popular car in America. I used Kelly Blue Book online and used the standard equipment that came on each vehicle. I selected the same features for each car from the same appraisal service to be consistent and to compare apples to apples. I let the computer figure out the average miles for this vehicle. I came up with the numbers listed to the right. This chart was written in the summer of 2005.

Figure 3

2000	5 Years Old	$ 7,340
2001	4 Years Old	$ 9,270
2002	3 Years Old	$ 11,105
2003	2 Years Old	$ 12,705
2004	1 Year Old	$ 15,085
2005	New	$ 20,997

FEES

There are two types of annual fees or expenses: inspection and registration. These vary from state to state and county to county. I decided to call the inspection $60.00 and the tag registration $36.00.

ANNUAL VEHICLE OPERATING COST

To find the cost of operating a car for a year in the U.S., consider the following table. I determined the depreciation of a 2005 Taurus by subtracting the value of a 2004 from the value of a 2005. Similarly, I subtracted the 2000 from the 2001 to determine the 2001 depreciation.

To find the gas mileage, I discovered the miles per gallon for a 2005 Taurus to be 20 around the city and 27 on the highway. I figured 23 mpg as an average for the year. I also chose 15,000 miles as the average number of miles driven. The 2001 is older and uses more gas, which is reflected in the consumption being higher for its 15,000 miles. After adding all of the costs, the 2001 model is $4,985.00 per year. Since it went 15,000 miles, $4,985.00 ÷ 15,000 = $.33 or 33¢ per mile. The 2005 Taurus is $8,403.00 ÷ 15,000 = $.56 or 56¢ per mile.

Figure 4

	2001	2005
Insurance	509.00	578.00
Gasoline	1,600.00	1,467.00
Repairs	700.00	200.00
Regular maintenance	150.00	150.00
Depreciation	1,930.00	5,912.00
Fees	96.00	96.00
Total	4,985.00	8,403.00

HORSE AND BUGGY

I have heard people say, when faced with the cost and responsibility of owning a car, "I am going to drive a horse and buggy and sell my car!" So I interviewed an Amish friend who has owned and driven a buggy for years to get some numbers. Here they are, minus the vet bills, which vary widely but are significant.

Figure 5

Used Buggy	3,000.00		
Average Horse	2,000.00		
Liability Insurance	90.00	per year	
Hay and Feed	912.50	per year	2.50 per day
Maintenance	150.00	per year	wheels, etc.
Depreciation	500.00	per year	
Shoes	279.50	per year	43.00 per 8 weeks
12 Volt Batteries	50.00	per year	for night driving

It is not as idyllic as it seems, is it? If he drives it 30 miles per week, times 52 weeks, 1,560 miles is his annual distance on the road. If a buggy and horse last 10 years, the depreciation is $500.00. Add this to the other annual expenses to reach $1,982.00 per year. Dividing this number by 1,560 miles, we find the cost per mile is $1.27. This is almost four times the cost per mile of operating a 2001 Taurus. One downside of having a horse is that even if he is not pulling your buggy, he still needs to be fed. But a positive aspect is that a horse has baby horses. That being said, it is difficult to compare road apples to road apples when comparing a horse and buggy with a car.

LESSON 16

Auto Mechanics

To understand the use of numbers associated with automobiles, I interviewed Mark, my friend and mechanic. We came up with four Ts to guide us in our study.

TOOLS

If you've ever done any work on an automobile, you've probably found out why mechanics have many tools, as well as how frustrating it is to switch from imperial to metric tools. Sometimes the chassis requires imperial measure tools and the engine requires metric tools. The disadvantage of imperial measurement is that the tools come in fractions of an inch. If a ⅜ inch wrench is too small, then instead of reaching for a ⅘ inch socket, you need ⁷⁄₁₆ inch, with the next larger being a ½ inch. Notice the sequence: ⅜, ⁷⁄₁₆, ½ . Now if you were using metric tools and a 10-mm wrench was too small, you would reach for an 11-mm, with the next larger being a 12-mm. Observe this sequence: 10 mm, 11 mm, 12 mm. Now, which looks more sensible and easy to use?

TIRES

A tire is the rubber portion of the wheel that is placed around a metal rim. The tire is the rubber that meets the road. Although tire companies often give their tires names, the way you compare tires and describe them is with a series of numbers. For example, if you see 195/65-15 on a tire, you can figure out all you need to know about that tire. The first number, 195, is the width of the tire in millimeters. The second number refers to the sidewall, or the part of the tire from the edge of the metal rim to the edge of the tire where it meets the road. This number is a percentage. In our example, 65 means 65% of the width of the tire. So 65% of 195 mm is 126.75 mm. The last number, 15, is the diameter of the rim in inches. Additionally, if a tire has reinforcement, it is referred to as a cross-ply or radial, depending on the way the reinforcement runs. If you see an R in the numerical description of a tire, it stands for "radial."

Figure 1

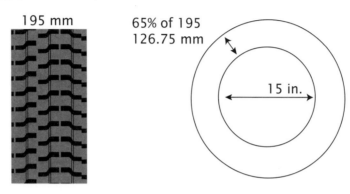

195 mm

65% of 195
126.75 mm

15 in.

Considering all of this information, what is the total diameter of the tire we have described, in inches and in millimeters? In example 1, we'll first change the millimeters to inches, then we'll do the reverse in the second part of the problem. (65% of 195 mm = 126.75 mm or 12.675 cm)

Example 1

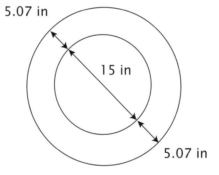

$$1 \text{ cm} = .4 \text{ in}$$
$$1 \text{ cm} = 10 \text{ mm}$$
$$12.675 \times 10 \text{ mm} = .4 \text{ in} \times 12.675$$
$$126.75 \text{ mm} = 5.07 \text{ in}$$

$$5.07 + 15 + 5.07 = 25.14 \text{ in diameter}$$

5.07 in

15 in

5.07 in

Another way to solve this is by using unit multipliers. (See references at the end of example 1.) Recall that 1 cm = .4 inches (or 10 mm is the same as .4 inches). The inverse is 1 inch = 2.5 cm. Using these two multipliers, we can solve these equations another way.

$$126.75 \text{ mm} \times \frac{.4 \text{ in}}{10 \text{ mm}} = 5.07 \text{ in}$$

The inverse of this problem, starting with inches, is seen in the following equation.

$$5.07 \text{ in} \times \frac{10 \text{ mm}}{.4 \text{ in}} = 126.75 \text{ mm}$$

$$15 \text{ in} \times \frac{10 \text{ mm}}{.4 \text{ in}} = 375 \text{ mm}$$

$$.4\overline{)15}^{\,37.5 \text{ cm}}$$

$$10 \text{ mm} = .4 \text{ in}$$
$$37.5 \times 10 \text{ mm} = .4 \text{ in} \times 37.5$$
$$375 \text{ mm} = 15 \text{ in}$$

126.75 + 126.75 + 375 = 628.5 mm diameter

Unit multipliers are taught in **Math-U-See Algebra 1.**
For purchase information visit **www.mathusee.com.**

TANKS

Tanks are the reservoirs of fluid in your vehicle. This information is important and is found in the owner's manual. Here are a few "tanks." Only one is actually called a tank, but I like the T.

Gasoline (or diesel fuel) tank
Oil capacity
Transmission fluid
Radiator
Windshield fluid

The first two are the ones you will use the most and the ones you ought to know about. If you know your gas tank holds 16 gallons and your oil capacity is five quarts, then it means something to you when you get a fill-up and it takes 15 gallons of gas and two quarts of oil. You were almost on empty, and your oil was dangerously low. So learn these so you won't be M-T (empty)!

TRAVEL

This section is a short tutorial on how to figure your gas mileage and speed. Gas mileage is becoming more and more of an issue as the price of gas rises. To figure out your miles per gallon, begin by filling your tank and recording the mileage in your odometer. For an example, let's say the mileage is 19,120. Then drive your car until you are ready to fill it up again. When you fill it, note how many gallons of gasoline you purchase. Let's say it is 12.3. Then record the mileage, which is now 19,375. Subtract 19,120 from 19,375 to get 255 miles. So you drove 255 miles using 12.3 gallons of gas. Dividing 255 by 12.3 equals 20.73, which is your miles per gallon. For every gallon of gas, you are driving 20.73 miles. If the price of a gallon of gas is $2.65, then $2.65 ÷ 20.73 = $.1278 or 13¢. Every mile you drive costs you 13¢ just for gasoline.

To get a more accurate reading, keep track of several tanks of gas. It is quite easy if you are on a long trip and filling up a couple of times a day. But if not, keep a book in the car and record the mileage and gas consumption, then figure it out for a longer period of time. The results will prove interesting. On longer trips, you generally get better mileage than you do in stop-and-go city traffic. You will also get better miles per gallon when driving on flat terrain than you will when climbing mountains.

Speed is computed in mph (miles per hour) or kmh (kilometers per hour). Your speedometer gives you this information, but sometimes it is not accurate, so here is a way to compute your speed using a watch and the mile markers along the road. If you are driving 60 mph, that is the same as 1 mile/1 minute or 1 mile in 60 seconds. The equation is D=RT where D is Distance, R is Rate, and T is Time.

Example 2

$$60 \frac{miles}{hour} = \frac{60 \ miles}{1} \times \frac{1}{1 \ hour}$$

$$60 \frac{miles}{hour} = \frac{60 \ miles}{1} \times \frac{1}{60 \ minutes} \qquad \text{Change 1 hour to 60 minutes.}$$

$$60 \frac{miles}{hour} = \frac{\overset{1}{60} \ miles}{1} \times \frac{1}{\underset{60}{3{,}600} \ seconds} \qquad \begin{array}{l}\text{Change 60 minutes}\\\text{to 3,600 seconds.}\end{array}$$

$$60 \frac{miles}{hour} = \frac{1 \ mile}{60 \ seconds} \qquad \begin{array}{l}\text{Divide numerator and}\\\text{denominator by 60.}\end{array}$$

$$\left(60 \frac{miles}{hour}\right)(60 \ sec) = (1 \ mile) \qquad \text{Multiply both sides by 60 sec (T).}$$

If your time decreases, it means you are going faster, or your rate (speed) is increasing. If your speed decreases, then it takes longer to get there, or your time is increasing. R and T have an inverse relationship. See the following two examples.

Example 3

$$R \cdot T = D$$

$$\uparrow \left(72\frac{\text{miles}}{\text{hour}}\right)\left(50 \text{ sec}\right) \downarrow = \left(1 \text{ mile}\right) = 3{,}600$$

The speed increases to 72, and now it takes you only 50 seconds to go one mile. 3600 (60 x 60) is the magic number for R x T. The rate times the time will always be 3,600 for one mile.

Example 4

$$R \cdot T = D$$

$$\downarrow \left(42\frac{\text{miles}}{\text{hour}}\right)\left(85.7 \text{ sec}\right) \uparrow = 3{,}600$$

The speed decreases to 42, and now it takes you 85.7 seconds to go one mile. $3600 \div 42 = 85.7$.

Now if you set your cruise control or maintain an even speed at 60 mph, watch the mile markers to go exactly one mile, while timing yourself in seconds. If it takes 60 seconds, your odometer is accurate. If it takes 56 seconds, then 3600 = R(56) $3{,}600 \div 56 = 64.3$ for the rate, and your speedometer is not accurate. You need to drive slower than the speed limit to be safe.

Example 5

If you are driving at a rate of 50 mph, how long will it take you to drive eight miles?

$$R \cdot T = D \qquad 50\frac{mile}{hour} = 50\frac{mi}{hr} \text{ and } \frac{1}{50\frac{mi}{hr}} = \frac{1\ hr}{50\ mi}$$

$$50\frac{mi}{hr} \cdot T = 8\ mi$$

$$\frac{1\ hr}{50\ mi} \cdot \frac{50\ mi}{1\ hr} \cdot T = 8\ mi \frac{1\ hr}{50\ mi}$$

$$T = \frac{8\ mi}{1}\frac{1\ hr}{50\ mi} = \frac{8\ hr}{50} \cdot \frac{60\ min}{1\ hr} = 9.6\ min$$

Example 6

If it takes 48 seconds to cover one mile, what is your rate of speed?

$$R \cdot T = D$$
$$R \cdot 48\ sec = 1\ mi$$
$$R \cdot 48\ sec = (60\ mph)(60\ sec) = 3{,}600$$
$$R = \frac{(60\ mph)(60\ sec)}{48\ sec}$$
$$R = 75\ mph$$

Insurance

When considering insurance, whether for health, home, or car, be led by a sound mind that considers the facts rather than by a spirit of fear.

I have noticed, when speaking with members of the insurance sales force, that they like to share stories of woe and despair. This "fear" of potential catastrophe is fostered to get you and me to buy more "insurance." God knows the past, present, and future. He doesn't want us to be fearful or unbelieving, but neither does He want us to be imprudent.

There is much to learn about the insurance industry. In this lesson we'll try to cover a few basic principles and some important terminology to prepare you for your insurance decisions in the future.

An insurance policy is a contract between you and an agency. You are required to pay a fee, called a premium, to the agency. They in turn are required to insure that your expenses or losses are reimbursed.

When choosing an insurance agent and/or agency, there are more factors to consider than just the price. But price is important, and it is a good idea to get several quotes from different agencies before making a final decision. A big factor in deciding which agent is a good fit for you is the agent's customer service, or how well the agent works with you and returns your calls. When a need arises, you want to be able to contact and work with your agent. Another factor is the agency's track record and financial solvency, both of which can be researched through your state insurance department or insurance commissioner. I have found it is beneficial to network, i.e., talk to friends and relatives to see whom they use for their insurance needs and why they have chosen those companies.

AUTO

Let's begin with auto insurance. All states have different laws governing their policies, but all of them have some form of requirement placed upon drivers to make sure they can cover costs if they are in an accident. The minimum insurance required by law is liability insurance. This is the bottom line and covers a person's basic responsibilities or liabilities in case of an accident. The numbers associated with liability are the limits an insurance company is required to pay in the event of a loss. When I was younger and had older cars, I carried only liability insurance, because the junkers I drove wouldn't be worth fixing in the event of a collision. But when I was able to afford a nicer vehicle, I made sure it was appropriately covered. Now I carry collision and comprehensive as well. We live in a litigation-happy world with many uninsured drivers on the highways. So now that I can afford more than the minimum, I consider it a good investment to have collision and comprehensive as well.

Liability insurance is 55% of the premium if you carry complete coverage. I asked my insurance agent to provide me with data from specific policies based on a few different variables. The results are found in the following charts. Study the charts and read the explanations of the numbers and categories. These are for a 51-year-old man who drives seven miles to work and back and has a clean driving record. After the three options are listed, there is an explanation of the terms.

Option 1

Coverage Option	Limit or Deductible	2005 Taurus
Split limits	100/300	103.00
UN Motorists	100/300	15.00
UND Motorists	100/300	45.00
Property Damage	100,000	71.00
PIP		26.00
Comprehensive	100 Deductible	54.00
Collision	250 Deductible	264.00
Total		**578.00***

*With a 250/500 deductible instead of 100/250, as it is currently, the total premium would be $542.00 instead of $578.00. If the deductible was 500/500, the premium would be lowered further to $532.00.

Option 2

Coverage Option	Limit or Deductible	2001 Taurus
Split limits	100/300	103.00
UN Motorists	100/300	15.00
UND Motorists	100/300	45.00
Property Damage	100,000	71.00
PIP		26.00
Comprehensive	100 Deductible	42.00
Collision	250 Deductible	207.00
Total		**509.00***

*With a 250/500 deductible the premium would be $481.00 and with 500/500, it would be $475.00.

Notice that the collision insurance is not significantly lower for a 2001 than for a 2005. The reason is that 90% of claims are for fender benders, which are not a total loss. They cost about the same to fix. A hood and fender replacement on a 2005 will require the same amount of work as on a 2001. The 10% that are total losses make up the difference in price, as it is more expensive to replace a 2005 than to replace a 2001.

Now if a 16-year-old is added to the original policy, see what the costs will be (option 3). By the way, with many companies, it is not possible for 16-year-olds to acquire insurance by themselves, as they are too much of a risk.

Option 3

Coverage Option	Limit or Deductible	2001 Taurus
Split limits	100/300	333.00
UN Motorists	100/300	17.00
UND Motorists	100/300	50.00
Property Damage	100,000	227.00
PIP		83.00
Comprehensive	100 Deductible	129.00
Collision	250 Deductible	600.00
Total		**$1,439.00***

If a student takes a driver training course, then the total premium is $1,380.00.

- Split limits (BI). This is for bodily injury. The two numbers 100/300 represent $100,000 and $300,000. The first number is the limit on the liability per person, and the second number is the limit per accident.

- UN Motorist means uninsured motorist.

- UND Motorist stands for underinsured motorist.

- Property Damage is for the damage you caused, whether it is to a utility pole or another car.

- Comprehehensive covers damage to the policyholder's car that did not involve a collision, such as damage from fire, explosions, earthquakes, floods, riots, and theft.

- Deductible is what you pay before the insurance company is obliged to pay. It is your responsibility. Here is an example. Let's say you have a policy with a low deductible of $50.00 You get a crack in your windshield that costs $450.00 to have repaired. The first $50.00 you pay out of your own pocket. This is deducted from the insurance company's responsibility, and they pay the remaining $400.00. The higher your deductible, the less the agency has to pay, and the lower your premium will be. If you decide to have high deductibles in your different insurance policies, be prudent and set aside money to cover the cost of the deductibles. Then if you need to pay them, you will have the necessary funds.

There are other common sense factors that affect the cost of your premium. The higher the value of your car or home, the higher the premium. How many miles you drive, how safe a driver you are (your accident record!), your age (older is cheaper!), and how much coverage you want will all affect your cost. Recently I learned from my insurance agent that as of this year (2005), your credit report is a major factor in getting insurance.

You can also get discounts by having more than one car insured by the same agent or by having your home insured as well. These are called multi-car and multi-policy discounts. Younger drivers can get discounts by completing driver education courses and having good grades.

HOME

Even though your home is worth more than the cost of replacing a car, it is not driving around at 60 mph, so the premiums are proportionately much less. The deductible does play a role. I asked for a quote for a 100,000-dollar house for several different deductible amounts, and this is what I got:

0 Deductible	516.00
100 Deductible	436.00
250 Deductible	372.00
500 Deductible	342.00
1,000 Deductible	312.00

Also, if you have your auto and home insurance with the same company, you can take an additional 15% off of your premium.

MEDICAL

When it comes to personal medical insurance, it seems like just about everyone needs a policy. Even if you don't plan on using insurance to cover regular doctor bills, an emergency may arise that could cost tens of thousands of dollars. It seems wise to carry coverage at least for these unforeseen and costly catastrophic needs. Today's health care costs are very high, and without adequate coverage you could lose all you possess paying for just one serious injury. While my faith is in God, I still think it is prudent to have coverage for emergencies. I have also found that doctors and hospitals in my area are willing to lower their charges as much as 30% if I pay cash instead of using an insurance carrier or a sharing plan. This year my wife had lab work done at a local hospital. The billing department deducted 60% because we paid with cash.

Sharing plans are not insurance but are an alternative to traditional medical insurance. There are personal lifestyle requirements to membership. Members pay, or share, each other's expenses. We have been a part of one for several years, and our bills have been paid when they have arisen.

Here are two websites for more information on sharing plans:
http://www.samaritanministries.org (Samaritan Ministries)
http://www.tccm.org (The Christian Care Ministry)

LIFE

Life insurance is like car insurance. You don't need car insurance unless you are in a wreck. Similarly, you won't need to cash in on your life insurance until you lose your life! Life insurance is marketed as a way to help family members upon your demise. It can pay funeral costs, probate expenses, and other significant outstanding debts, like college loans or mortgages.

There are several types of life insurance. The two main categories are permanent and term. Permanent life insurance requires you to pay a premium (like other insurance) for a death benefit, as well as for a savings account. As long as you pay your premium, your survivors receive compensation (death benefit) when you pass away. The compensation is the face value of the policy, say $50,000.00. But the policy is also a savings account, in that you are building equity by paying into your account. This is called the cash value. Traditional life insurance doesn't pay very good returns on your money, but you do have a growing nest egg to tap into if emergencies arise. You will have to reimburse the fund, but it is a type of reserve for you.

Term life is cheaper because you are renting a policy instead of owning one. If you purchase a term policy for 15 years and continue to pay your premiums, your beneficiaries would receive the face value of the policy when you die. But if after 15 years you are still alive, there is no cash available. Your rental agreement has run out. Term life is likened to renting a home, while permanent life is compared to owning a home, although real estate will generally appreciate and bring a much better return than a life insurance policy.

I found a lot of helpful information on the different types of insurance at the Insurance Information Institute. They may be found at http://www.iii.org.

"For God hath not given us the spirit of fear; but of power, and of love, and of a sound mind" *2 Timothy 1:7, KJV.*

Real Estate

Recently a real estate agent named Ervin took time out of his busy schedule to meet me for lunch. I plied him with questions for 1 ½ hours. As with other lessons in this book, an exhaustive study of real estate would take months, so I'm going to focus on only a few key applications for the average home buyer.

RENT OR OWN

Whether to rent or to buy is the obvious first consideration. If you live in an area with a strong economy, then buy a house because its value will most likely increase, or appreciate, while you live in it. If the economy is weak, consider renting unless you find a super deal. A weak economy means your home will not increase in value, and you won't be able to recoup the costs associated with buying and selling a home. There are many factors that will influence your decision, but that is the rule of thumb. Usually your mortgage payment will be comparable to your rent payment, and you will be investing in an appreciating asset (if the economy is strong). This is an asset that increases in value over time. Even if the rent payment is $600.00 and the mortgage payment with taxes and insurance is $725.00, the amount you can write off on your taxes will offset the 125-dollar difference.

Some reasons for renting are that the landlord has all the responsibility for fixing plumbing problems, painting the exterior, replacing damage after a storm, etc. It is his house. He also has to pay the property tax bill and not you. But, if you stay there five years, you leave and he still owns the house.

The advantages of buying your own place will vary according to the individual. But sheer economics will tell you that owning your own home is the main way most people set aside money for retirement. This will be your personal estate. Real estate will be one of your safest investments, and one that has historically appreciated over time. Plus, unlike renting, which leaves you no return, when you make your house payments you are putting the money into something that you own.

If you are buying or selling, should you do it yourself or go through a real estate agent? Even Ervin, who is an agent, lists his properties with other agents and doesn't do it himself. His advice was that you will make more money, have less frustration, and buy or sell a home in the timeliest manner with the aid of a professional. If you are a buyer, having someone who specializes in the buying and selling of real estate is also critical. Home buying is the biggest single investment you will ever make. Enter into it carefully and prayerfully, with the help of an expert.

Another factor to consider is how much to pay. Ervin recommends you pay no more than 30% of your monthly income. If you make $2,000.00 per month, the most you should spend is $600.00 per month for housing.

STATE COMMISSIONER

I live in Pennsylvania where there is a State Real Estate Commission. It is always a good idea to contact them before entering into contracts to find out the rules and regulations governing the sale of real estate in your state.

SALES COMMISSION

In Pennsylvania, the listing agent or the one selling the property receives a 3% commission. The agent representing the buyer, or buyer broker, gets 3% as well. This is negotiable and may vary from agent to agent. On a $100,000.00 house, each agent would receive a commission of $3,000.00. Sometimes the fee is 4% for the listing agent and 3% for the buyer broker, for a total of 7%. Other times it is 2% for the selling agent and 3% for the buyer broker, or 5%. But 6% is the mean and the mode. These fees are paid by the seller.

POINTS

Points are 1% of the amount of the loan. They are prepaid interest on the amount you are borrowing. For example, if you want to borrow $100,000.00 at 6%, you can lower the percentage of the loan by prepaying the interest. The idea is, if you pay more up front, your monthly payment will be lower. This money you are paying up front will generally lower the rate of your loan between $\frac{1}{8}$ and $\frac{1}{4}$ of a percent per point. So if you pay one point, then the 6% loan may drop to 5⅞% or 5¾%. That will lower your monthly payment from $599.55 to $591.54 at 5 ⅞% or $583.57 AT 5¾%. To find out if this is a good use of your money, divide $1,000 (one point) by 8.01, the ⅛% discount on your loan. $1,000 ÷ 8.01 = 125. So it will take you 125 payments or a little longer than 10 years to recoup the one point or $1,000.00 in prepaid interest. If the bank gave you ¼% off, it will take 62.6 payments or five years to recoup your $1,000.00. If you are going to stay in the home for a long time, it may be worth it, but if you are not sure, put the $1,000.00 towards your principal instead of prepaying the interest, which you will learn more about later.

Figure 1

Interest Rate	Points	Loan	Monthly Payment	Save per Month
6%	0	100,000.00	599.55	
5 ⅞%	1	100,000.00	591.54	8.01
5 ¾%	1	100,000.00	583.57	15.98

CLOSING COSTS

In closing, we come to the closing costs, all of which are negotiable. These vary from state to state and county to county, but when in doubt—ask! In our area there is a 2% transfer tax, 1% going to the state and 1% to the county. Then there are credit application fees and a charge for an independent appraisal. Courts charge to record a deed, as does the notary. If the seller has already paid the property taxes for the coming year, these are prorated and added to the bill.

An important item for the buyer to remember is to contract with a title company to research and verify that it is a clear title. There may be liens on the property. A lien is the right of a creditor to collect money from the sale of your real estate. It is an obligation that the owner of the house has been unable to pay. So in lieu of getting their money they place a lien on the house. Then, when the house is sold, they get their money. An example might be the government collecting back taxes or a hospital trying to collect payment. If there are liens, the title is not free and clear. If you aren't careful, you may end up buying the seller's house and his debts! Since liens can take time to work their way through the bureaucratic red tape, title insurance ($775.00 on a $100,000.00 loan) covers you and the title company in the event there is an outstanding obligation. So pay for the title insurance; it is worth it. Closings are often scheduled for the end of the month to avoid an additional payment on your mortgage. A mortgage is a long-term loan for a house, usually 15 to 30 years in length.

On the following chart notice how much of the initial payments go to the interest on the loan and how little to the principal or amount of the loan. An amortization table is a detailed payment schedule showing the total amount and the principal in each payment. It is in your best interest to pay extra on your monthly payments, especially at the beginning. In the following example, we'll show four ways to pay off the 25-year, 5% mortgage on $100,000.00: monthly, monthly plus $50.00, monthly plus $100.00, and biweekly. By adding that little extra each month, you whittle away at the principal more quickly and save money in interest. A monthly amortization schedule would have 300 columns, one for each month or each payment, but we will just give the first three and last three payments for each schedule, as well as their total amounts. Notice the amount of interest and the length of each loan.

Figure 2

Mortgage for $100,000.00 over 25 Years at 5% Interest Standard Monthly

Balance	Payment	Principal	Interest	Payment
100,000.00	584.59	167.92	416.67	1
99,832.08	584.59	168.62	415.97	2
99,663.46	584.59	169.33	415.26	3
(Skip Ahead to final 3)	584.59	....	....	....
1,739.26	584.59	577.34	7.25	298
1,161.91	584.59	579.75	4.84	299
582.16	584.59	582.16	2.43	300
0				

from loan calculator

Total # Payments	300
Total Interest Paid	$75,377.01
Total Principal Paid	$100,000.00

Figure 3

Mortgage for $100,000.00 over 25 Years at 5% Interest
Standard Monthly plus $50.00 additional each month

Balance	Payment	Principal	Interest	Payment
100,000.00	634.59	217.92	416.67	1
99,782.08	634.59	218.83	415.76	2
99,563.25	634.59	219.74	414.85	3
(Skip Ahead to final 3)	634.59	....	....	....
1,295.58	634.59	629.19	5.40	256
666.39	634.59	631.81	2.78	257
34.58	34.72	34.58	.14	258
0				

Total # Payments		258
Total Interest Paid		$63,124.36
Total Principal Paid		$100,000.00

Figure 4

Mortgage for $100,000.00 over 25 Years at 5% Interest
Standard Monthly plus $100.00 additional each month

Balance	Payment	Principal	Interest	Payment
100,000.00	684.59	267.92	416.67	1
99,732.08	684.59	269.04	415.55	2
99,463.04	684.59	270.16	414.43	3
(Skip Ahead to final 3)	684.59	....	....	....
1,778.38	684.59	677.18	7.41	224
1,101.20	684.59	680.00	4.59	225
421.20	422.96	421.20	1.76	226
0				

Total # Payments		226
Total Interest Paid		$54,455.71
Total Principal Paid		$100,000.00

Figure 5

Mortgage for $100,000.00 over 25 Years at 5% Interest
Biweekly (26 payments per year for 21+ years)
    Total interest paid $63,203.19 ≈ 566 payments

Extra payment per year (13 payments per year for 21+ years)
    Total interest paid $63,243.93 ≈ 283 payments

The biweekly payment option means you are paying half of the monthly requirement every two weeks. In our example that would be half of $584.59, which is $292.30. By paying every two weeks, you end up paying an extra monthly payment for each year. A normal payment option is one payment per month, or 12 payments per year. But you aren't simply doubling that to pay two per month or 24 for the year, you are paying 26 payments each year, which is how you are making an extra payment annually. This is the difference between semimonthly and biweekly. You aren't paying two per month (semimonthly) but every two weeks (biweekly). I do not have an amortization schedule broken down for each payment, but at the end of the loan, you will have paid $63,203.19 in interest, and be done paying the mortgage in a little over 21 years instead of in 25 years.

I also ran the numbers in the mortgage calculator to see if you would have the same results by just making 13 monthly payments per annum instead of 12. The interest on that mortgage is $63,249.93, or a little difference of $46.74, for the same time frame. If you consider that if you have to mail 283 more biweekly payments at 44¢ per stamp (an additional $124.52), it is more cost-effective to just make one extra monthly payment each year instead of a biweekly payment every two weeks. ☺

Contracting and Painting

There are certain home maintenance jobs that I have felt my family and I could take care of ourselves. They include painting, landscaping, cutting the grass, washing cars, and washing windows. There are others that we learned how to do; like building fences, decks, retaining walls, and sheds. There is a sense of satisfaction that comes from doing home maintenance and simple construction yourself. Each family has to determine what they can and cannot do themselves. There are other jobs, such as electrical, plumbing, and gas line installation, that I am not competent enough to do, not to mention the fact that they could also cause potential danger and damage if not done properly. Fortunately, God has provided trustworthy and qualified men to do this work for us, and I am glad to hire their services. There are other skills, like hanging and finishing Sheetrock, that I can do; but professionals—guys who do it every day—are so much quicker and more efficient that it pays to hire them.

For example, in our current home, I mudded, sanded, and finished the drywall in our living room. It took me several evenings, was a lot of work, and I still didn't get it to look smooth. Then I found a man who lives on our street who finishes drywall for a living. When I had him finish the game room, he came down for a few hours, spread out over several days, and did a great job for $100.00. That was the end of my drywall finishing. Even though I can do it, I can't do it well, or efficiently.

When you do hire contractors, here are some tips to keep in mind:

1. Remember that you are hiring them; you are the boss. If they are questionable, say "No, thanks," and interview someone else

to do the work. It is your house. Don't give in to any pressure from them.

2. Check with your friends and neighbors to find reliable workers and construction firms.

3. If you need to hire someone from the yellow pages, and he is unknown to you or your associates, ask for references from previous customers. Follow through and call these people or drive over and inspect his work. If this offends him, say good-bye. Better to do your homework first and not have to learn a painful lesson.

4. Check with your state government about the credibility and competence of a contractor. Ask if he is certified. Not all contractors have to be, but some professions require certification.

5. Whether you know them or not, make sure the workers are insured or bonded. Otherwise, if they get hurt on the job, you are responsible for their bills. With no insurance, even if they say they will accept responsibility, you are still responsible.

6. When you choose a contractor, don't assume anything. Get your expectations in writing as well as the estimates. By expectations, I mean write out what you want done. An estimate or a bid from the contractor should also be spelled out in writing. Get several estimates to help you get an idea of what the job is worth.

7. Make sure you both understand how you will pay. Is it half up front for materials and the rest when the job is done, or is it payment in full after the job is completed? There are many different ways to do it; make sure you are clear. If his proposed payment schedule sounds fishy, tell him you'll get back to him and check it out with some close, experienced folks who can give you good sound counsel.

8. Decide whether you are paying by the job or by the hour. If it is by the job and you have the price, make sure there is a date of completion. I would suggest you never pay for work in full until you have inspected it and are completely satisfied that it is done. If they have the final check, you have no leverage and you will probably never see them again.

9. If you are paying for labor plus materials, which means you pay for the materials and an hourly rate for the contractor's time, find out when the clock starts. Recently some carpenters who did some work for me billed me from the time they left their home till they got home that evening. I got eight hours of work and was billed for 10 hours. They only worked one day!

10. Don't be afraid to ask questions. If you and your spouse have any concerns, remember, you are doing the hiring. If you are uncomfortable, don't get involved with a contractor in the first place. Everyone has their horror stories as well as their glowing reports of working with contractors. I hope these tips help you have more positive than negative experiences.

ESTIMATES

When I was finishing some improvements on my warehouse, I asked for an estimate of what it would cost to put metal siding on two sides. The contractor gave me a figure of what he thought it would cost him to do the work. He figured how much time it would take him to do the job and how much the materials would cost, and then he gave me a price, or quote. This was his estimate—the amount he estimated the job would cost. If he wanted to call it a bid, he would put it in writing and that would be his fixed price for doing the job. A bid, or contract, is what he will be paid regardless of how long it takes, and he is committed to his original price. The good part for a contractor with a bid is that if all goes well, he may do very well. But if the job runs into a snag, or the weather doesn't cooperate, or the price of materials goes up, he could lose money on a project.

I used estimates and bids on the work that was done. During the course of the renovation, I got to know several of the contractors very well and developed a relationship of trust with them. So even when I got their bids and estimates, I told them to charge me the fair value for their time and materials. That way I didn't pay too much and they don't lose any either.

I learned firsthand about estimates and bids as a painting contractor. After my initial experience as a painter of gutters and high trim I decided to pursue painting full-time the next summer, so when I came home after my first year in college, I began painting houses. I hired some local guys to work for me. I figured the estimates and gave the homeowners my price and then paid my workers an hourly wage. I got paid by the job. My workers got paid by the hour. They had no risk and were paid regardless of how long it took to complete the job. But the better we worked, the more I made per job. As the contractor I had the potential to make more, and also to lose more. I was paid for taking that risk.

PAINT

My father, who sold paint to department stores, used to tell me there was a lot of information on a paint can. Besides telling you what kind of paint to use and how to prepare the surface before painting, you also learn about coverage. Coverage, or how many square feet the paint will cover, depends on the surface. If you are painting a rough surface, the paint will not cover as much as on a smooth surface. For smooth interior walls you can expect at least 400 square feet per gallon. Make sure you find out if the paint will require one coat or two. My rule of thumb for buying paint is to buy the high quality brand. The difference between cheap paint and high-quality paint is only a few dollars compared to the time for your labor in getting ready to paint and then actually doing it. Plus, a good paint may need only one coat, or application, of paint, whereas a cheaper brand will probably take at least two coats. A few more dollars for paint is worth the savings in labor. The same applies to painting the exterior of a house. Buy good paint and good brushes and don't cut corners in that department. The time you save will more than offset any savings in inferior materials or brushes.

Coverage: If you paint a bedroom that is 12 ft x 15 ft with 8 ft ceilings, you will need about one gallon for the walls and ½ gallon for the ceiling. See example 1 for how to figure this.

Example 1

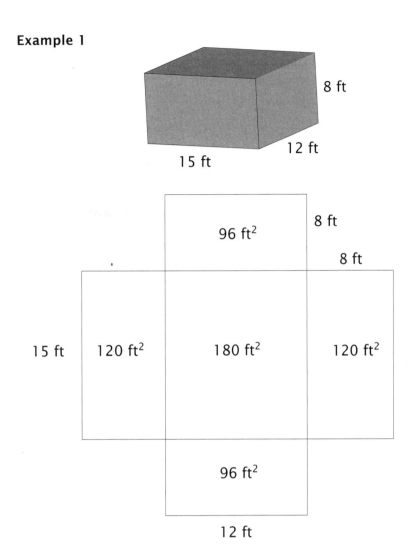

Ceiling: 180 ft^2
Walls: 96 + 96 + 120 + 120 = 432 ft^2

When you are buying paint, you may find that three individual quarts cost the same as one gallon. If a gallon covers 400 square feet, then a quart will cover one-fourth of that, or 100 square feet. Two quarts will cover 200 square feet, which is enough to do a ceiling 12 ft x 15 ft. If my ceiling had been 250 square feet, I would have had to decide whether to buy two quarts or one gallon since the job would require a little over half a gallon of coverage. Sometimes you can stretch paint to cover 125 square feet per quart, but you don't want to run short, so I would opt for the gallon. If a quart of paint is priced at $7.95, then a gallon would be three times that, or $23.85. This is not necessarily true in all stores. Recently I bought paint at

Home Depot, and found that their price for a quart was $10.99 and for a gallon was $21.99. At that store, two quarts, not three, is the same price as one gallon. So be sure to check this when buying paint.

A SQUARE

Shingles are generally figured by the square. A square is 100 square feet or 10 ft x 10 ft. If your house has a roof that is 40 ft x 18 ft on each side, as in example 2, the area would be 40 ft x 18 ft = 720 ft x 2 sides = 1,440 ft^2. We find 1,440 ÷ 100 = 14.4. So you will need 15 squares to cover 1,500 square feet, since 14 squares would not be enough.

Example 2

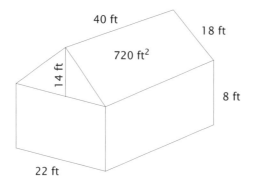

Siding is also measured by the square. In example 2, the area of the walls is 8 ft x 22 ft on each end and 8 ft x 40 ft on the long sides. Each triangular gable end is 22 ft wide and 14 ft high, and has an area of 1/2 x 22 x 14, or 154 square feet. Since there are two of these, they add up to 308 square feet. 176 + 176 + 320 + 320 + 308 = 1300 square feet. When you divide this by 100 square feet (a square of siding is 100 square feet) you get 13, so you need 13 squares of siding to complete the job.

CONCLUSION

It is worth repeating that the cost of materials is proportionately less than the cost of labor in the twenty-first century. When I painted houses for several summers, I observed that homeowners who grew up in the Depression era were very frugal but unwise when they tried to save money on paint. I grew up in an area where most of the homes had brick, stone, or aluminum siding. So to paint a house with mostly windows, a few doors, some overhang, and a garage door only took two to three gallons of paint. A good-quality paint might cost $20.00 per gallon. So the total cost of materials would be $60.00. The labor to do this job would be $400.00 to $500.00. Often the homeowner would buy a cheap paint and save $15.00 to $20.00 total. But that paint would not last as long as the good stuff, and the house would need to be repainted a year or two sooner. So saving $20.00 in materials actually cost them a few hundred dollars in increased labor charges.

Seventy-five years ago the cost of materials was a large part of the job. Materials are still a significant part of any job, but today the cost of labor has risen so dramatically that the cost of materials is not as significant as it once was. My advice is to not skimp on quality paint, shingles, or siding unless you absolutely have to. You will be better off in the long run!

Rent, Fabric, and Carpet

One of the issues young homeowners (or renters) face is whether to buy certain tools or rent them. There is no one answer to this question, so we will explore a couple of guidelines and specific situations to help you think through the issues. There is a third option that looks great to some people and not so great to others— borrowing from a friend or a relative. I heard of a man who was seen carrying several tools into his neighbor's garage. The neighbor asked him what he was doing, since he hadn't asked to borrow those particular tools. The man replied that he just wanted to have all of his tools in one place! Obviously the neighbor had taken advantage of his friend and abused the privilege of borrowing.

BORROW

Let's explore borrowing first. The best-case scenario is when you borrow a tool, you use it carefully, it doesn't break, you clean it and return it promptly with a hearty thanks. The job is complete and you are happy and your neighbor is relieved to have his tool back where it belongs. The worst-case scenario is that you borrow the tool, it breaks, you buy your neighbor a replacement, and then you have to buy or rent the same tool to finish the job. All of the other cases fall in between those two. You may forget to return the tool and funny feelings develop in your relationship with your neighbor. Or, you return the tool dirty or somewhat damaged and don't offer to fix it. Or, while you are using the tool, the owner has a need for it but can't use it because it is at your place. In case you are not keeping score, that is one good scenario and four not-so-good ones. In my experience, for most cases, it is not a good idea to borrow tools except in emergencies, assuming you value relationships more than dollars and cents.

Guideline #1. If you need a tool or appliance that you will use again but just haven't gotten around to purchasing, buy it now. Determining the quality of the item and how much you will spend depends on your situation. My brother used to make his living with tools. So if he needed a certain tool, he spent the extra money to make sure he had a high-quality one. I, on the other hand, like to have tools on hand for handyman jobs but know that I don't need the best available. Middle-of-the-road is good enough for me.

Guideline #2. If it is an expensive item that you use only occasionally, rent it. I power wash the siding on my home twice a year. To rent a high-pressure power washer costs $70.00 a day. To buy the same one would cost over $2,000.00.

Dividing the $70.00 into $2,000.00, you can see that I would have to use the power washer 28 times for this to be a good investment. Plus, when I rent it, the rental company stores the machine, maintains it, and keeps it running efficiently. The power washer rents for $49.00 for four hours, $70.00 for a day, and $177.00 for a week.

While I was getting these figures from our local Grand Rental Station, I asked Mike and Steve which item was rented the most frequently. Their answer was the carpet cleaner, which rents for $19.00 for four hours, $29.00 per day (24 hours), and $87.00 per week. A new carpet cleaner retails for over $1,000.00. Think how often you clean your carpets, and you can see what a great deal it is to rent instead of own. There are less expensive models you can buy, but I am pricing the same model as the one in the store.

Guideline #3. Here is a final thought on purchasing items for your home and family use. When you are considering buying a bed, remember that you will spend one third of your life using it. But if you are considering buying a tuxedo, take into account the fact that you may wear it only once a year or once every five years. Identify the items that you use every day, like a bed and shoes, and contrast them with tuxedos and carpet cleaners, and purchase accordingly. Some items are made to be rented.

FABRIC

Recently I visited a local department store to see how mathematics was used in the fabric department. An associate named Patti graciously took me through the different rows of material. The first thing I noticed was how they were presented on the shelves. A bolt of fabric is wound around a cardboard center, which is how most of the fabrics are presented. There is also a good bit of material that is on sale and not on a bolt but lying in stacks on a shelf or table. It is referred to as flat fold. Cloth is sold by the yard which is 36 inches, or 3 feet, in length, but the width varies. The most common width is 45 inches, but there are also 54-inch, 60-inch, and even 72-inch widths. A yard of 45-inch fabric is 36 inches by 45 inches. A yard of 60-inch material is 36 inches by 60 inches. The width may vary, but the length is still one yard.

I'm going to focus my attention on the three most common fabric shoppers: quilters, crafters, and seamstresses (those who make clothes to wear). According to Patti, quilters usually look first at the flat fold material, which was sale priced at $1.99 per yard (45 inches wide). Then they go to the broadcloth, or calico prints, which are 100% cotton and were priced at $5.89 per yard. Crafters often buy felt, which goes for $4.19 per yard and is 72 inches wide. This material has a variety of uses, such as posters, banners, and boards for teaching children in a classroom setting. Seamstresses tend to purchase a fabric blend of polyester (65%) and cotton (35%). This was priced at $3.69 per yard and comes in 54-inch widths.

Figure 1

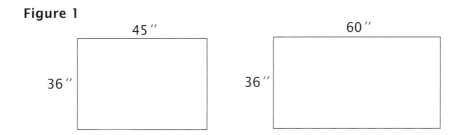

CARPET

My wife and I have bought carpet several times from Sam's store in town. He has been in the business for a long time and understands it well. Besides possessing a wealth of information, he is also a consummate salesman.

As with the other lessons in this book, I am simply going to take a quick look at this topic. Carpet quality is determined by its face weight, or the weight of the nylon in one yard. A good face weight is 35 oz. This is not wool carpet, but nylon, which is the material most commonly used for carpet. Another question to ask when shopping for carpet for your home is whether the nylon is a continuous thread. If it is 100% continuous nylon, it will be as long wearing as steel (according to Sam).

To learn about the quality of carpet and the proficiency of the installer, it is worth developing a rapport with a local dealer. The average price for a good quality carpet can vary, but Sam's best-selling carpet goes for $15.00 per yard. Since most of us don't know how to install carpet, we must also pay the price for installation, which is 60¢ per square foot (or $5.40 per square yard). Notice how 60¢ per square foot sounds better than $5.40 (9 x 60¢) per square yard. Sam's store recommends a good-quality padding, which is 90¢ per square foot or $8.10 per square yard. Carpet is measured by the yard. This means a square yard, which is 3 ft x 3 ft, or 9 square feet, or one square yard.

Example 1
Find the cost of carpeting a room that is 12' by 15'.

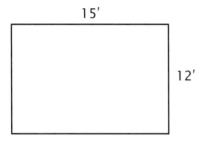

Since carpet is sold by the yards, first figure out the number of square yards. 15' ÷ 3' = 5 yards, and 12' ÷ 3' = 4 yards. So the room is 4 yards by 5 yards or 20 square yards.

Carpet $15.00 x 20 = $300.00
Padding $8.10 x 20 = $162.00
Installation $5.40 x 20 = $108.00

Total cost:
$300.00
162.00
+ 108.00
$570.00

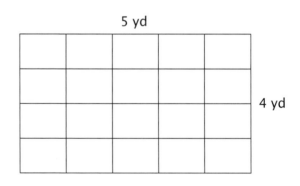

The total cost, $570.00, when divided by 20 yards, is $28.50 per square yard. This in turn can be divided by 9 to find $3.17 per square foot. Now you will find carpet that is cheaper than this and some that is more expensive, but this is a good benchmark. May all your carpet lie flat and last long!

Concrete and Stone

As of March 2005, the price for a cubic yard of concrete was $83.50. A cubic yard is 1 yd x 1 yd x 1 yd, or 3' x 3' x 3', so there are 27 cubic feet in one cubic yard (figure 1). When talking with someone in this field, you will not hear them say "cubic yards." Instead they will say "yards," even though they are referring to cubic yards. A tri-axle truck typically holds 11 yards of concrete, or 11 cubic yards, or 11 yd^3.

Figure 1

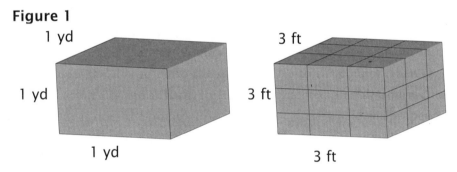

If you want to pour a foundation using one yard of concrete and make it one foot deep, you will have 27 square feet on the top of your pad (figure 2).

Figure 2

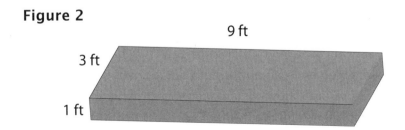

If you want it six inches (one half foot) deep, you still have 27 cubic feet, but now you have 54 square feet on the surface (figure 3).

Figure 3

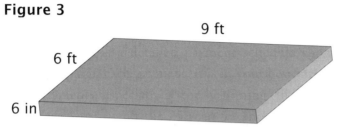

$$1/2' \times 6' \times 9' = 27 \text{ ft}^3$$

A yard of wet concrete weighs about 3,750 pounds. If the yard is dry, with just the cement, sand, and stone, it weighs 3,500 pounds. A standard concrete mix uses 500 pounds (500#) of cement, 1,200 pounds of sand, and 1,800 pounds of crushed stone or gravel.

Gravel and sand both weigh about 100 pounds per cubic foot. Therefore a ton is about 20 cubic feet of sand and gravel mix. (20 cubic feet times 100 pounds equals 2000 pounds or one ton.)

When you call to order concrete, you will be asked to specify a number for the type of concrete you need. This number measures pounds per square foot, or the amount of weight the concrete will bear. The higher the number the more cement you get, as well as a greater weight capacity and a higher price. The numbers go from 2,500 to 3,000 to 3,500 and on up in increments of 500. 3,000 is strong enough for sidewalks and patios, but 3,500 is recommended for driveways and garage floors. The price of $83.50 per yard I quoted in the beginning of the lesson is for 3,500.

Grade	Price per Yard
2,500	79.00
3,000	82.00
3,500	83.50
4,000	85.00

GRAVEL

I called a company that delivers gravel to job sites to ask questions about weight and volume. I learned that they use a ratio for figuring this relationship. It is 1.4 tons per cubic yard. With this info I was able to figure out the reverse, or yards per ton, simply by applying what we know about fractions and unit multipliers from *Algebra 1*. There are 1.4 tons per one cubic yard, and one cubic yard per 1.4 tons, since both ratios are equal to one.

$$\frac{1.4 \text{ tons}}{1 \text{ yd}^3} = \frac{1 \text{ yd}^3}{1.4 \text{ tons}} = 1$$

To change yards to tons use the first ratio, and conversely, to change tons to yards use the second ratio.

Example 1
Change 21 tons to yards.

$$\frac{21 \text{ tons}}{1} = \frac{1 \text{ yd}^3}{1.4 \text{ tons}} = 15 \text{ yd}^3$$

Example 2
How many truckloads are required to carry 35 yards of gravel to a job site?

$$\frac{35 \text{ yd}^3}{1} \times \frac{1.4 \text{ tons}}{1 \text{ yd}^3} = 49 \text{ tons}$$

49 tons is 49 times 2,000, or 98,000 pounds.

On the first page of the lesson we found that a truck can carry 11 yards of concrete, which weighs 3,750 pounds per yard. So a truck can carry 41,250 pounds. To carry 98,000 pounds you would need two full trucks and another partial one, so three trucks are needed.

WATER

In the spring I often call a water delivery service to fill up our pool. The name of the company is cool: Jacob's Well. It is not named after the biblical Jacob, but after the owner, Jacob Glick. They have trucks with the capacity to carry 4,000 gallons or 6,500 gallons of water. One gallon of water weighs 8.35 pounds, and there are 7.48 gallons in a cubic foot. So how much does a cubic foot of water weigh? 7.48 x 8.35 = 62.458, or rounded up, 62.5 pounds.

Example 3

How many cubic feet of water in a 4,000 gallon truck?

$$\frac{4,000 \text{ gal}}{1} \times \frac{1 \text{ cu ft}}{7.48 \text{ gal}} = 534.76 \text{ cu ft}$$

Example 4

How many gallons of water will my tub hold if it is 4' long by 2' wide by .75' deep? How much will the water weigh?

$$4 \text{ ft} \times 2 \text{ ft} \times .75 \text{ ft} = 6 \text{ cubic feet}$$

$$\frac{6 \text{ cu ft}}{1} \times \frac{7.48 \text{ gal}}{1 \text{ cu ft}} = 44.88 \text{ gal}$$

$$\frac{44.88 \text{ gal}}{1} \times \frac{8.35 \text{ lbs}}{1 \text{ gal}} = 374.5 \text{ lb}$$

LESSON 22

Plumbing and Electrical

In plumbing, when you are moving liquid, the size of the pipe determines how much liquid can move through it. And even though you may think this is a volume issue, it is really the area of the circle, or the cross-section of the pipe, that determines the flow.

In the first example we are comparing the areas of two circles, one with a diameter of two inches and the other with a diameter of three inches.

Example 1

 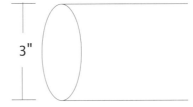

$$A_{2"} = \pi r^2 = \pi(1)^2 = 3.14 \text{ in}^2 \qquad A_{3"} = \pi r^2 = \pi(1.5)^2 = 7.065 \text{ in}^2$$

Notice that even though three inches is only 50% larger than two inches, the area of the three-inch diameter circle is almost double the area of the two-inch diameter circle. This is because we are squaring the radius before multiplying by pi, which is represented by π and has a value of 3.14.

I recently made a trip to our local hardware store to confirm that with a two-inch pipe, the two inches is the measure of the opening. It is not the external but the internal measure. See figure 1.

Figure 1

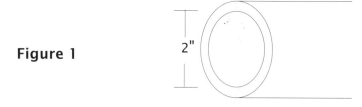

In heating and air conditioning, the critical measurement is the area of the cross-section of the duct (which could be a circle, oval, or rectangle). The area determines the flow. Compare the area of a six-inch air duct with an eight-inch air duct. In the six-inch duct the radius is three inches or half of the diameter. In the second duct the diameter is eight inches, so the radius is four inches.

Example 2

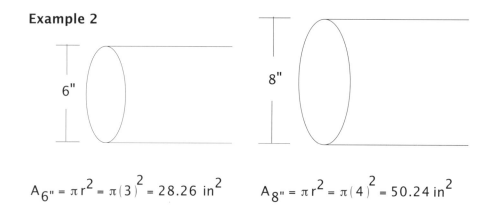

$$A_{6"} = \pi r^2 = \pi (3)^2 = 28.26 \text{ in}^2 \qquad A_{8"} = \pi r^2 = \pi (4)^2 = 50.24 \text{ in}^2$$

Using a pipe just 33%, or ⅓, larger yields an air flow that is almost double, or 100% greater. Don't trust your eyes; do the math and you will see that it is true.

ELECTRICITY

Electricity is both a source of energy and a convenience. Many Americans heat their homes with electricity (instead of oil or gas) and have come to rely on these little electrons moving across wires for everything from lights to computers and even cars. In this unit we will study a formula for the basic electricity used in your home and try to make sense of an electric bill.

There are three terms in the electrical formula V x A = W. The letter V is for volts, A is for amps (sometimes I is used for amps), and W is for watts. Volts times Amps (short for amperes) equals Watts.

$$V \times A = W$$

Volts — pressure of electricity
Amps — amount of electricity
Watts — usage of electricity

A home in the U.S. generally has 120 volts moving along the wires to the outlets, appliances, and light fixtures. The number on the top of your light bulbs is the number of watts. The larger the number, the more watts, and the brighter the light. In our home we use mostly 60-watt bulbs and occasionally 40- and 75-watt bulbs. Twenty-five watts is used for decorative fixtures, and 100-watt lights in our basement fixtures round out our usage. Here is a one-sentence description of the three components: amps, watts, and volts. Amount of electricity (amps) pushed by the pressure (volts) yields the power usage or quantity (watts). For a 100-watt light bulb, you would use .833 amps since the voltage is a constant 120. See the equation in example 1.

Example 3

$$V \times A = W$$
$$120 \times A = 100$$
$$\frac{120}{120} \times A = \frac{100}{120}$$
$$A = .833$$

To check :
$$V \times A = W$$
$$120 \times .833 = 100$$
$$100 = 100$$
$$\text{Volts} \times \text{Amps} = \text{Watts}$$

Most homes in the U.S. today are set up with what is called a 100-amp service. Older homes may have had a 60-amp service. We certainly use more electricity today than 50 years ago. So with 100 amps and 120 volts you could supply a home with a 12,000-watt capacity.

Example 4

$$V \times A = W$$
$$120 \times 100 = W$$
$$12{,}000 = W$$

Now if you are an electrician and are planning the circuits in a home to run from a breaker box, you would need to add up the watts and find out how many amps are needed. Most appliances will have this information on a panel somewhere. If you have a circuit that includes a refrigerator (approximately 500 watts), a toaster (1,050 watts), and a microwave oven (800 watts), would it fit on a 15-amp or 20-amp breaker box? If there is too much current running through a line, it could overheat and potentially cause a fire. When the line is overloaded, the breaker box "breaks," and then you know you have a problem. Another factor is that appliances use much more electricity when they start up than while they are running. It is, therefore, a good idea, if you have a black-out or a brown-out (power failure), to turn off major appliances and then turn them on one at a time so they do not turn on simultaneously and overload your circuits.

Example 4 calculates which size breaker the refrigerator, toaster, and micro-wave require. In your service panel, where the electricity enters your home from the power company, you will see several breaker boxes. Some will say 15, others 20, and a few 30. These are measured in amps. The big ones, 30 for example, are for appliances that use large amounts of electricity, such as an electric range, an electric dryer, or a heat pump/air conditioning unit. The smaller 15-amp breakers are for regular usage around the home. A 15-amp breaker has a maximum capacity of 1800 watts.

Example 5

$$V \times A = W$$
$$120 \cdot 15 = W$$
$$1,800 = W$$

The rule of thumb is to take 80% of maximum capacity (or 20% less than 100%) for what is called safe capacity. 1,800 x .80 = 1,440 watts. So a 15-amp breaker has a safe capacity of 1,440 watts.

Example 6

Refrigerator	500 W
Toaster	1,050 W
Microslave ☺	800 W
	2,350 W

$$V \times A = W$$
$$120 \times A = 2,350$$
$$\frac{120}{120} \times A = \frac{2,350}{120}$$
$$A = 19.6$$

It looks like a 20-amp breaker is in order, since 19.5 would fit onto a 20-amp breaker. But we haven't considered the safety factor. The safe capacity is 80% of full capacity, and 80% of 20A equals 16A. So even though 19.5 is less than 20, it is more than 16, so it is not enough. The electrician will have to put one of these appliances on another circuit. A lot of math is used in the electrical field, but this study is done to whet your appetite for more. Interview an electrician yourself and see if he can show you more applications of math!

MY ELECTRIC BILL

The following chart is a copy of a recent electric bill. The reason this bill is broken down into the specific charges is that after the industry was deregulated, they were required to "unbundle" the bill! The two main numbers and symbols you will see as you read it are cents and KWH. Cents are given in large decimal numbers. KWH stands for one kilowatt hour. Kilo is 1,000, so kilowatt represents 1,000 watts per hour.

Charges for PPL Electric Utilities	
Residential Rate	
Distribution charge:	
Customer Charge:	8.00
200 KWH at 2.193¢ per KWH	4.39
600 KWH at 1.984¢ per KWH	11.90
518 KWH at 1.862¢ per KWH	9.65
PA Tax Adj. Surcharge at .088%	.03
Transmission Charge:	
1,318 KWH at 0.5640¢ per KWH	7.43
Transition Charge:	
200 KWH at 1.329¢ per KWH	2.66
600 KWH at 1.178¢ per KWH	7.07
518 KWH at 1.088¢ per KWH	5.64
PA Tax Adj. Surcharge at .064%	.01
Generation Charge:	
Capacity and Energy	
200 KWH at 5.182¢ per KWH	10.36
600 KWH at 4.554¢ per KWH	27.32
518 KWH at 4.178¢ per KWH	21.64
PA Tax Adj. Surcharge at .088%	.05
Total PPL Electric Utilities Charges	116.15

Notice the breakdown. The first 200 KWH are computed at one rate, then 600 KWH have a different rate, then everything beyond that has a lower rate. The customer charge is for accounting, measuring, monitoring, maintenance costs, and equipment. The transmission charge is what you pay to get the electricity to your company from the company generating the power. The transition fee (which may eventually disappear) is the charge to recover your utility company's investment in power sources. The generation expense is for the production of electricity and is the most expensive charge on your bill.

To find the price I pay for each KWH, add up the total KWH, in this case 1,318, and divide it into the total charges, which are $116.15. The average price per KWH for the month is $.088.

$$1{,}318 \overline{)116.14} \quad .088 \qquad 8.8\text{¢ per KWH}$$

This is almost nine cents per hour. So if you leave ten 100-watt light bulbs on for one hour it will cost you nine cents.

Humble Pie and Lumber

A tried and proven way to save money is to not buy new. There are certain things that you will want to purchase brand spanking new, like shoes and underwear, but if you can eat a little humble pie and buy used, you will find some great buys. Here are some suggestions, after you pray. Remember, a man's life consists not in the abundance of the things which he possesses *(Luke 12:15)*.

Garage sales, yard sales, and estate sales are wonderful places to find used items. When our children were younger, we would be praying for a bicycle or cowboy boots, and then we would see a sign or an ad for a garage sale. More often than not we would find just what we were looking for at a very affordable price. It was so remarkable that I had to remind our kids that our faith was in God and not in yard sales. But God did use them a lot in our experience. We also found it to be helpful, if we had some time and could plan ahead, to shop at yard sales in upscale neighborhoods. For us this meant an hour drive or more, but it was worth the effort. We observed that there are two types of people that hold sales: those who are trying to make money from their junk, and those who are trying to clean out their houses and are happy to make a few bucks in the process. We found more of the latter in the nice suburbs. They would sell nice name-brand stuff at a fraction of the price. When you go to a yard sale, don't be afraid to dicker a little. Make an offer; all they can say is no. More on this in the next lesson.

We also found a lot of our larger items such as appliances and furniture in the classified section of the paper and in the penny saver or advertiser in our area. Many people want to upgrade and will sell for a bargain their used items that have plenty of life left in them. We did this for years and found we saved thousands of dollars in the process. We were blessed to see God guide our steps, and we enjoyed the adventure.

Don't overlook the many thrift, new-to-you, or consignment stores, such as Goodwill. These have regular hours and also carry nice things.

TIPS FOR EATING OUT

As you may have figured out, we lived on a pretty tight budget for many years raising four boys. During that time, we made many long car trips attending church functions, visiting relatives, and going on vacations. For a while we made sandwiches, put them in the cooler, and ate in the car. But I decided that didn't make for much of a trip, especially for my wife. So we began eating out. Here are some tips we found that made it possible for us.

1. Drink water, not soft drinks. I haven't seen the profit sheets of a restaurant, but I am willing to bet that most of their profit is in the drinks they offer. Carbonated drinks cost pennies, yet they are sold for upwards of a dollar and are half ice. (Recently, I spoke to a lady who used to work in a nice, well-established local restaurant. She was told that they made 25 cents on the entrees and the rest of the profit came from drinks and desserts.)

2. If you do get lemonade or a soda, request no ice. If you want to get a drink, get one, not ice.

3. Forego dessert, which is an expensive item with little or no nutrition. If you must have one, share a large one among your family. Desserts are pricey!

4. An obvious tip is to buy items on sale. Many times we would walk into an Arby's and get 10 regulars and six waters. They used to run a special of five regular sandwiches for $5.55. Our family of six ate for $11.10. That is hard to beat even if you make your own food.

5. I think the best deal for a large family today is Boston Market. It is a cross between a restaurant and a fast food joint. You order your food, sit down, and eat it right there. The food is excellent: they have chicken, turkey, and meat loaf. You can choose from a wide variety of vegetables. It will feed the lot of you, and you won't pay

more than $25.00—less if they are having specials. If you go to a McDonald's and each of you orders a combo meal for around $4.50, you will spend more money for burgers, carbonated drinks, and deep-fried cholesterol sticks. Another big savings in each of these choices is not having to pay tips.

6. For those special times when you do get to eat at a nice place, remember points 1 through 3. And when you are figuring your costs,add at least another 20% to the cost of what you order. Tips are 15% to 18%, and then you have food tax, which can be from 4% to 8%, depending on where you are eating. If there are six of you and each of your meals is $12.99, your final bill will be at least $90.00. Six times $12.99 is $77.94, plus 5% tax — $3.90 — plus a 16% tip — $12.47 — which equals $94.31. And that total is assuming you are all drinking water. If you add drinks at $1.49 each and a dessert at $4.99 apiece, then your total is $116.82 for food, plus $5.84 for tax and $18.69 for the tip for a grand total of $141.35. There is quite a difference between $141.35 and $94.31. If you eat frugally, you can dine at a restaurant three times at $94.31 for the same price as two times if you order drinks and dessert.

LUMBER

When you purchase lumber for a construction project, you will find that the name or size of the piece does not match the actual dimensions. One of the most popular pieces of wood used in building is the 2 x 4 (pronounced two by four). You would think it would be 2" x 4" but it is really 1 ½" x 3 ½". When it was first cut at the lumber mill it was 2" x 4", but after planing and finishing all the way around, it arrives at the finished dimension of 1 ½" x 3 ½".

Figure 1

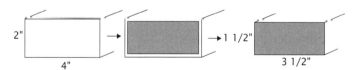

Similarly, a 1 x 4 turns out to be ¾" x 3 ½" and a 2 x 6 is 1½" x 5 ½" See the chart in figure 2 for more sizes and actual dimensions.

Figure 2

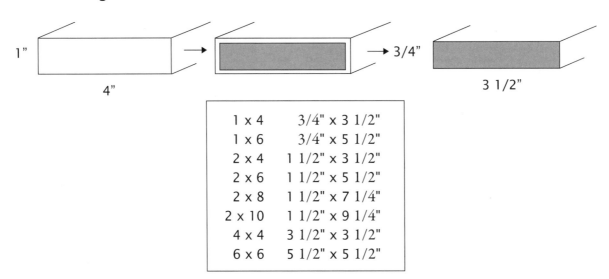

1 x 4	3/4" x 3 1/2"
1 x 6	3/4" x 5 1/2"
2 x 4	1 1/2" x 3 1/2"
2 x 6	1 1/2" x 5 1/2"
2 x 8	1 1/2" x 7 1/4"
2 x 10	1 1/2" x 9 1/4"
4 x 4	3 1/2" x 3 1/2"
6 x 6	5 1/2" x 5 1/2"

You will also find man-made building materials that are called by the same sizes or names as wood products. I like to use vinyl for fencing since I don't have to paint it. It is close in price to wood and a lot easier to maintain. A vinyl piece that measures ¾ inch x 3½ inches is still called a 1 x 4, and if it is 3½ inches x 3 ½ inches it is called a 4 x 4. The same is true of pressed board materials that are used in construction but are composed of man-made substances or wood chips.

MAKING CHANGE

Recently, I visited our local farmers' market. A hundred years ago there were seven in our town, but now there is only one, and it is open three days per week. When you go there you will notice the absence of computers and even cash registers in many of the booths. When you sell an item from a stand with no electronic machinery, you have to be able to "make change." In talking with a few different enterprises there, I found this skill is becoming a lost art. So if you ever get a job and have to make change, you should know how to do so. By the way, I was in a Wendy's one day for lunch when there was a power failure. No one at the front counter knew how to figure change without the aid of a machine. Finally they found a girl in the back who was peeling potatoes who came to their rescue. It is a useful thing to be able to add and subtract without the aid of a cash register or calculator, and then make change.

Example 1

Let's play act. You are a worker at Shenk's Poultry and someone buys an assortment of chicken that comes to $3.27. They give you a 10-dollar bill. What do you do?

You could subtract $3.27 from $10.00 and get $6.73 and then give them back their change. Or you could count it back to them by saying, "Three twenty-seven, three thirty, three fifty, four, five, and five is ten." What you are doing is starting with the amount they purchased and adding up to $10.00 in increments of coins and dollars.

Start with "three twenty-seven."
   Place three pennies in their hand and say "three thirty."
   Place two dimes in their hand and say "three fifty."
   Place two quarters in their hand and say "four."
   Place a one dollar bill in their hand and say "five."
   Place a five-dollar bill in their hand and say "and five is ten."

You are beginning with the amount they purchased and adding up to $10.00 in increments of coins and bills.

Example 2

This time the amount of the sale is $1.83 and they give you a five-dollar bill.

$5.00 − $1.83 = $3.17.

Start with "one eighty-three."
   Place two pennies and say "one eighty-five."
   Place one nickel and say "one ninety."
   Place one dime and say "two" or "two dollars."
   Place three dollar bills and say "three, four, and five."

You begin with $1.83 and add up to $5.00 in increments of coins and bills.

Example 3

The next customer owes you $14.08 and gives you a 20-dollar bill.

$20.00 minus $14.08 equals $5.92.

Start with "fourteen oh eight."
   Place two pennies and say "fourteen ten."
   Place one nickel and say "fourteen fifteen."
   Place one dime and say "fourteen twenty-five."
   Place three quarters and say "fifteen."
   Place a five-dollar bill and say "twenty."

You begin with $14.08 and add up to $20.00 in increments of coins and bills.

Haggling and Insulation

Negotiating the cost of an item is very difficult for some and like breathing for others. I have some friends who are so good at it, I am embarrassed to go shopping with them. I have other friends who wouldn't think about doing it. I am in the middle. But first a little history.

In many parts of the world today this is still the way you do business. It also used to be the way to conduct business in the United States. As I understand, one of the first men to offer prices on price tags was John Wanamaker in Philadelphia. He felt that because he was a Christian this was a more honorable way to sell retail goods. Then others like Woolworth followed suit. We take price tags for granted, but you won't find them in much of the world. I took a trip to Thailand recently where dickering is the accepted way of purchasing. But there is a certain way to do it. Now I don't pretend to be an expert in the art of dickering, but here are a few points that I have learned.

1. Be polite and treat the sales staff as you would like to be treated. Avoid being rude and contentious. The Lord's servant must not strive, but be gentle towards all *(2 Timothy 2:24)*.

2. Find out the approximate price of the item by going to several vendors and shopping. I found a wide range of prices for the same item on the same street in Thailand, from 290 bahts to 480 bahts. In U.S. dollars that is $7.70 to $12.70. Know what the standard starting price is before you begin to dicker. In other words, do your homework. You aren't trying to cheat them. You just want to arrive at a place where you are both happy. This should be a win-win situation!

3. Talk to the locals to find out what is a good place to begin bidding. Where I was recently, if you make too low an offer, they are offended. But if you bid too high, then you have no room to negotiate. The rule of thumb was that you should pay a third less than they were asking. So if the price they ask is $300.00, then you should aim at $200.00. Your starting price might be $150.00 or $160.00. Then they counteroffer, and thus begins the haggle.

I was in Jerusalem years ago and was leaving the city when a boy offered me three hand-carved olive wood camels. I didn't want them and kept walking, smiling, and telling him no thanks. He persisted until the price lowered to $2.00. Now for that price I couldn't refuse, and I bought them. They made a nice gift. The next day I was in the Old City where there were shops selling the same camels. I innocently asked what the price was and was told something like $15.00–$20.00. To this day I still wonder what the real cost of a set of camels is.

My first experience haggling in the U.S. was when I was renting a large moving truck. I went to a Ryder Truck rental place and got their offer. It was so much per day, plus a price for each mile. Then I called U-Haul and Hertz-Penske. All I remember is that I got prices from all three and eliminated one. Then I called the first place back and told them I was going with another bidder. He then asked me what price I had received and lowered his price to beat it. These two companies went back and forth a few times until I got the best price. I saved hundreds of dollars with just a few phone calls.

SHOP AROUND

One fall when I had a remodeling project I made a list of exactly what I needed, then called five lumber yards to get quotes, not only on the items but also on delivery options. When I got the best price and was ready to buy, one of them called and said they would match the lowest price and deduct another 10%. That was pretty tough to beat. And once again the savings were significant.

PRAY

When we were finishing off our current home, we had two experiences where God multiplied our dollars. The first was when we were looking for flooring. We wanted some kind of hardwood floor for health reasons but found it quite expensive. As we prayed and shopped, we found a furniture factory that had odds and ends of maple in different sizes and lengths. We bought skids of this wonderful wood for $5.00–$10.00 per skid. When I am looking to repair pieces I have to pay that much per foot. We spent more for the stain and polyurethane than we did for the wood.

KEEP EARS AND EYES OPEN

The doors and windows in our house had no casement trim, nor was there any baseboard trim. Someone told us of a place that sold trim in six- to seven-foot lengths for $1.00. That is about 16¢ per foot. The going price for the same material new was at least 69¢ to 79¢ per foot. So we backed our good old van into the lumberyard and loaded hundreds of sticks for a fraction of the price. We had to do some piecing in some areas, but we received significant savings.

INSULATION

Another set of numbers you encounter in most building or remodeling projects is R-value. This is a measure of how effective your insulation is. According to the Department of Energy, 50%–70% of the energy used in the average American home goes to heating and cooling. Twenty percent is used for heating water, and 10%–30% is used for appliances, lighting, computers, and everything else. R-value stands for thermal resistance, or the resistance to heat flow. The higher the R-value, the greater the effectiveness of the insulation. When you buy insulation you will see this number on the packaging. If, for example, your attic has a blown-in substance that gives you an R-value of 27, but you want more R-value, you can either blow in some more or lay fiberglass sections on top of the blown-in material. If the fiberglass gives you R-13, then you add the values to get an overall R-40 for your attic.

There are several different materials and options for insulation. The most common is fiberglass, which is usually pink and advertised by the Pink Panther. You will also find yellow fiberglass insulation. It comes in pieces that are flat or in long rolls that can be placed between the studs in your walls, between the ceiling rafters, or between the floor joists. Some of the advantages are that fiberglass does not absorb moisture and is noncombustible. A 9 ¼-inch thick piece has an R-value of 30. See the chart for other values and thicknesses.

Fiberglass	
Thickness	R-Value
3 ½"	R-13
5 ½"	R-21
9 ¼"	R-30

Then there is blown-in cellulose, which is ground-up newspaper. It is blown in through a hose and is moist to help it stick to the wall between the studs. One inch of this material has an R-value of 3.84. The thicker it is, the more R-value you have, and the less heat will escape. The big advantage of this kind of insulation is that it goes in quickly, a crew can do a home in a day, and it doesn't leave any air pockets. It is also cheaper than the next option and you don't get pieces of fiberglass in your eyes or on your skin. Here are a few values arrived at by simple multiplication.

Cellulose	
Thickness	R-Value
3 ½"	R-13.4
5 ½"	R-21.1
9 ¼"	R-35.5

The neatest stuff is polyurethane foam, which I have had put in my warehouse. It dries almost instantly and is hard when it does. There are no air pockets since it fills up all of the space, because when it hardens and dries, it expands. One inch of this material gives an R-value of 9 when it is installed and 7 after 20 years. The R-7 is a conservative figure. I will pick 8 as the average to compute the values for our chart.

Polyurethane Foam	
Thickness	R-Value
3 ½"	R-28
5 ½"	R-44
9 ¼"	R-74

Example 1
Our ceiling had no insulation. The rafters were 2x10s. We had cellulose blown in until it was level. What is our R-value?

A 2x10 is 9 ¼ in thick.
9 ¼ in times 3.84 for cellulose equals R-35.52.

Example 2
At the warehouse we had ¾ of an inch of polyurethane foam sprayed on, then the rest of the 2x6 wall filled with cellulose. What is the R-value of my walls?

¾ times 8 equals R-6 for the foam.
A 2x6 is 5½ in thick, minus ¾ in (foam) equals 4¾ in.
4¾ in times 3.84 for cellulose equals R-18.24.
R-6 plus R-18.24 equals R-24.24

On the Road

Whenever I travel, I find multiple opportunities to use math skills. Since I live in the U.S., I encounter less familiar metric measures in distance (kilometers), temperature (Celsius), and exchange rates with the currency of the country I am visiting. Of course these are reversed for someone visiting the U.S. So take a little trip with me and we'll examine distance, temperature, and currency.

SPEED AND DISTANCE

In the country we are visiting, we rent a car and are driving down the road when we see a sign informing us that the local speed limit is 50 km/h. How fast is this in my native mph, or miles per hour? There are two ways of figuring the answer: quick or accurate. The quick way is to multiply 50 by .6 to get 30 mph. The accurate way is to multiply 50 by .625 to get 31.25 mph.

The key ratio in changing kilometers to miles is 8 to 5. We'll see where this originates in Figure 1. Eight kilometers is very close to five miles. Most cars today in the U.S. have a speedometer that has this ratio, in case you forget. Find where it reads 50 mph and you'll see an 80 km/h right above or below it. Fifty mph to 80 km/h is the same as 5 mph to 8 km/h. And remember that a kilometer is a little over half a mile, or .625 mile. We'll do some ratios with these set as equal to one another to find our conversion numbers.

Figure 1

Divide them both by 8 to find out how many miles are in 1 kilometer.

$$8 \text{ km} = 5 \text{ mi}$$
$$\frac{8 \text{ km}}{8} = \frac{5 \text{ mi}}{8}$$
$$1 \text{ km} = .625 \text{ mi}$$

Or divide them both by 5 to discover how many kilometers are in 1 mile.

$$8 \text{ km} = .625 \text{ mi}$$
$$\frac{8 \text{ km}}{5} = \frac{5 \text{ mi}}{5}$$
$$1.6 \text{ km} = 1 \text{ mi}$$

Example 1

Change 50 km/h to m/h, or mph.

$$50 \frac{\cancel{km}}{hr} \times \frac{.625 \text{ mi}}{\cancel{km}} = 31.25 \frac{mi}{hr} = 31.25 \text{ mph}$$

To do this in your head while driving is difficult. It's much easier to simply multiply 50 by .6 instead of .625 for a quick and fairly accurate number. 50 times .6 is 30 mph, which is close to 31.25.

This same ratio of eight kilometers to five miles works in distances on road signs as well. If the town you are heading for is 200 kilometers away, then multiply it by .6 and recognize you are about 120 miles away.

Example 2

Change 60 mph to km/h.

$$60 \frac{\cancel{mi}}{hr} \times \frac{1.6 \text{ km}}{1 \cancel{mi}} = 96 \frac{km}{hr} = 96 \text{ km/h}$$

QUICK TEMPERATURE CONVERSION

As you drive, you might be interested to know the temperature and notice that the radio tells you it is 20°. Once again, there is accurate and there is quick. The specific formula is that for every 5°C, there is a corresponding 9°F plus 32°. In our example we divide 20° by 5, which is 4°, multiply that by 9 to get 36°, and add 32° for 68°F. But again, this is pretty tough as you are driving. The quick estimate method is to double 20°C and add 30°. So 20° x 2 = 40° and 40° + 30° = 70°F, which is pretty close to 68°.

Accurate

$$(C° \div 5 \times 9) + 32° = F°$$
$$(20° \div 5 \times 9) + 32° = F°$$
$$(4° \times 9) + 32° = F°$$
$$(36°) + 32° = 68°$$

Quick

$$(C° \times 2) + 30° = F°$$
$$(20° \times 2) + 30° = F°$$
$$(40°) + 30° = 70°$$

To see how we reached this answer, consider the formula. Dividing by 5 and multiplying by 9 is ⁹⁄₅. The ⁹⁄₅ is 1.8, which is almost 2, and 30 is a little less than 32. The little bit you are over in multiplying by 2 instead of 1.8 you compensate for by adding 30, which is a little less than 32.

CURRENCY

When you travel to a country with a different currency, there are a couple of considerations. First find out how best to transport funds. Twenty-five years ago it was recommended that you use traveler's checks, which you could get from a bank or AAA (American Automobile Association). Then when you traveled you would exchange them at a place of business or at the hotel where you were staying. But now in many countries these are hard to cash and you are often charged a fee to do so, so it is easier to use an ATM (Automated Teller Machine). ATMs also give you the best rate of exchange for your money.

The second consideration is finding the place that gives you the best exchange rate. At airports you will see businesses behind glass booths offering to exchange your money. These are convenient but pricey. You pay for the convenience. Talk to your travel service, and if you can, people who live in that country. Gather information wherever you can. It may change from year to year and country to country.

Here are three currencies that you may run into. And while having a calculator is the most accurate way of changing money and recognizing a good value, it is not as rewarding as doing it in your head. In many countries you haggle for the best price. Understanding how to estimate costs in terms of local currency gives you an advantage in your negotiations.

EURO

This currency is used in an ever-expanding number of countries in Europe, hence the name. On May 5, 2005 (or 05-05-05), the value was one dollar for .77256 euros. To find the value of one euro, divide both numbers in the second fraction by .77256 and you find one euro is 1.2944 dollars.

$$\frac{1 \text{ dollar}}{.77 \text{ euros}} = \frac{.77 \text{ euros}}{1 \text{ dollar}} = \frac{1 \text{ euro}}{1.29 \text{ dollars}} = \frac{1.29 \text{ dollars}}{1 \text{ euro}}$$

When I look at these numbers I round them to one dollar equals 75 cents (in euros), and one euro is $1.30. If I see an item for sale that is 25 euros, I calculate that it is 25 times 1.3 in order to make it dollars. One times 25 is 25, and .3 times 25 is 7.50, and 25 plus 7.50 is 32.50. Even if you use a calculator, you still need to estimate the price to double check your computations.

YEN

This type of currency is used in Japan. One dollar equals 104.52 yen. To find the value of one yen, divide both numbers in the second fraction by 104.52 and you find it is 0.09568 dollars.

$$\frac{1 \text{ dollar}}{104.52 \text{ yen}} = \frac{104.52 \text{ yen}}{1 \text{ dollar}} = \frac{1 \text{ yen}}{.009568 \text{ dollars}}$$

It seems a yen is just a little less than a penny. So it is a simple matter of moving decimal points. If something is marked for sale at 34,000 yen, then think, "This is 34,000 pennies, which is $340.00." But since a yen is a little less than a cent, it is less than $340.00. Do you have a yen for this kind of math?

STEWARDSHIP

RUPEE

Rupees are the currency of India. One dollar equals 43.525 rupees. To find the value of one rupee, divide by 43.525 and you find a rupee is equivalent to .02298 dollars.

$$\frac{1 \text{ dollar}}{43.525 \text{ rup}} = \frac{43.525 \text{ rup}}{1 \text{ dollar}} = \frac{1 \text{ rupee}}{.02298 \text{ dollars}}$$

A rupee is 2.3¢. This is not as neat as the others, but it still can be useful in estimation. If you see an item for sale at 1,300 rupees, move the decimal point two places as you divide by 100 to make it $13.00. Then multiply 13 by 2.3: 2 x 13 = 26, and .3 x 13 = 3.9. Finally, 26 + 3.9 = $29.90.

Keeping Score

All sports are concerned with numbers simply in order to keep score and to measure accomplishments. Without covering every sport, I have chosen a few to show how math is applied. If you would like to contribute information about a sport you enjoy, and how you use math in it, send it to Steve@mathusee.com.

Track and field measures distance and time. In the U.S., yards were used for generations, but meters are now often used here, as in the rest of the world. If you encounter older records, you will still see the 100-yard dash instead of the 100-meter dash, and ¼ mile or 440 yards instead of the 400 meters.

Golf is a game where the lowest score wins. Players keep track of the number of strokes needed to play 18 holes. Seventy-two strokes to play 18 holes, or an average of four strokes per hole, is the norm at many golf courses. Par is usually 4. This number is based on the length and difficulty of a hole, and is the number of shots recommended for one hole. If a hole is longer it may be a par 5, and if shorter, a par 3. The length of a hole is measured in yards. An average par 4 may be 300–400 yards, while a par 5 will be at least 400 yards, and a par 3 may be only 150–250 yards.

If a player takes three shots on a par 4 hole, that is called a birdie. A birdie is one less than par. An eagle is two strokes below par and is better than a birdie. If you get an eagle on a par 3 (3 - 2 = 1), you just got a hole-in-one! An eagle on a par 5 is a 3 (5 - 2 = 3). One stroke more than par is a bogey, and two strokes above par is called a double bogey.

If you watch a tournament you will hear the announcers say a player finished at three under par with 2 bogies and 5 birdies. This means he had 5 x (-1) for birdies or - 5, and 2 x (+1) for the bogies, so -5 plus +2 equals -3 or three below par. The score card below is for 18 holes. How many birdies, eagles, bogeys, and double bogeys are there?

Hole	1	2	3	4	5	6	7	8	9	Out
Par	4	5	4	4	4	4	3	4	4	36
Score	4	4	5	4	6	4	3	4	3	37

Hole	10	11	12	13	14	15	16	17	18	In
Par	5	4	4	3	4	4	3	4	5	36
Score	3	4	4	3	5	5	2	4	6	36

On the front nine, or first nine holes, there are 2 birdies (#2 and #9), 1 bogey (#3), 1 double bogey (#5), and 5 pars for a score of 37. The first 9 is referred to as "Out" because you are leaving the clubhouse. "In" is when you are returning to the clubhouse on the back 9.

The back 9 has 1 eagle (#10), 1 birdie (#16), and 3 bogeys (#14, #15, and # 18) for a 36. For the 18 holes, the golfer is one over par, or +1 for the day.

BOWLING

Now, if it's raining and you want to go indoors, bowling awaits you. I am familiar with three kinds of bowling: ten pin, which has 10 large pins and large 10-16 lb balls thrown two per frame; duckpin, which has little squat pins and small balls also thrown two per frame; and candlepin, which has tall, thin pins and small balls thrown three per frame instead of two per frame as in ten pin and duckpin.

If you roll your ball and knock down all the pins in one shot, you get a strike, which is a score of 10 and is recorded with an X. But the best part of a strike is that you get the 10 pins for your score, plus the number of pins you knock down with your next two balls. I remember this by the two slashes required to make an X. If you knock down all of the 10 pins but it takes two rolls to do so, it is called a spare and is recorded with a slash /. On a spare, you are rewarded with the 10 pins knocked down, plus the pins on your next roll (1 slash = 1 roll). If you don't get all 10 pins with two balls, this is called an open frame and your score is simply the number of pins knocked down.

Here are some examples of a bowling score sheet. Unfortunately, in this age of computers, most bowling alleys do not use paper score sheets; instead the computer on the lane you are bowling records your scores on an overhead monitor.

Sandi	✕		3	6	7	/	9	–
	19		28		47		56	

Frame		Activity
1	✕	Sandi rolled a strike with her first ball.
2	3 6	She rolls a 3 on the first ball and a 6 on the second. So she gets 10 + 3 + 6 (the sum of her 2 balls plus 10 for the strike) = 19. Then you add the 9 to that, 19 + 9 = 28 for the score in the second frame.
3	7 /	Her first ball is a 7, then she gets 3 more (the rest of them) for a spare (one slash).
4	9 –	The first ball is a 9, so in the 3rd frame 10 (for the spare) + 9 is added to 28 for 47. Then she misses the remaining pin, so 9 is added to 47 for a score of 56.

BASEBALL

Baseball is crazy about statistics. Here are four that you will run across if you follow this sport: batting average, slugging percentage, earned run average, and win-loss percentage.

Batting average is the number of hits divided by the number of at bats (AB). If you get 2 hits in 6 at bats, your average is 2 divided by 6. This is always recorded as the first three places of the decimal number. You will hear people say a player is batting 300. This means .300. For 2 hits in 6 at bats, your average is $2 \div 6 = .333$, which is better than .300.

Batters are also interested in their slugging percentage, which is tricky to compute. This is a statistic that is computed by dividing the number of at bats into the total number of bases. Over a five-game period, Lou Gehrig hits 3 singles, 1 double, 2 triples, and 1 home run in 24 at bats. His slugging percentage is .625 and his batting average is .292. During the same period, Pee Wee Reese gets 6 singles and 2 doubles (8 hits) in 24 at bats. His slugging percentage is only .417 but his batting average is .333. See their statistics in example 1.

Example 1

Lou Gehrig

Type of Hit	# of Bases	Quantity	Total Bases
Single	1 Base	3	3
Double	2 Bases	1	2
Triple	3 Bases	2	6
Home Run	4 Bases	1	4

$$\frac{\text{Total Bases}}{\text{At Bats}} = \frac{15}{24} = .625 \qquad \frac{\text{Hits}}{\text{At Bats}} = \frac{7}{24} = .292$$

Pee Wee Reese

Type of Hit	# of Bases	Quantity	Total Bases
Single	1 Base	6	6
Double	2 Bases	2	4
Triple	3 Bases	0	0
Home Run	4 Bases	0	0

$$\frac{\text{Total Bases}}{\text{At Bats}} = \frac{10}{24} = .417 \qquad \frac{\text{Hits}}{\text{At Bats}} = \frac{8}{24} = .333$$

Babe Ruth has the highest lifetime slugging percentage of .68972 or 690.

Pitchers are associated with their ERA and win-loss percentage. ERA stands for earned run average. This is the number of earned runs per nine inning game. If Nolan Ryan gives up 4 runs in a full game, his ERA is 4.0. If Dizzy Dean gives up 2 runs in only 3 innings, his ERA is 6.0. The formula is earned runs times 9 divided by innings pitched. The thinking is that if Dizzy had kept pitching and giving up 2 runs in every 3 innings, he would have yielded 6 runs in 9 innings.

Example 2

Nolan Ryan

$$\text{ERA} = \frac{\text{Earned Runs} \times 9}{\text{Innings Pitched}} = \frac{4 \times 9}{9} = \frac{36}{9} = 4.0$$

(For one game)

Dizzy Dean

$$\text{ERA} = \frac{\text{Earned Runs} \times 9}{\text{Innings Pitched}} = \frac{2 \times 9}{3} = \frac{18}{3} = 6.0$$

To compute a pitcher's won loss percentage, or W-L %, add up the wins and divide them by the total number of games pitched. At the end of the season Nolan was 18-10 or 18 wins and 10 losses. Dizzy got his fast ball back and went 21-7 for the year.

Nolan Ryan

$$\text{W-L\%} = \frac{\text{Wins}}{\text{Games Pitched}} = \frac{18}{18+10} = \frac{18}{28} = .64 \text{ or } 64\%$$

(For the season)

Dizzy Dean

$$\text{W-L\%} = \frac{\text{Wins}}{\text{Games Pitched}} = \frac{21}{21+7} = \frac{21}{28} = .75 \text{ or } 75\%$$

TENNIS, ANYONE?

Tennis keeps score much differently from other sports. In a match, the first player to win six games wins the set. We'll begin with a game. If you win 1 point you are said to have 15 (or in some places 5). If you win another point your score is 30, and the third point is 40. If you are 2 points ahead of your opponent and you win the fourth point, you win the game. You have to win by 2 points. But if you are tied at 40 all, you are said to be at "deuce." You continue to play until either you or your opponent goes up by 2 points. At this point a new language enters the picture, called advantage or ad. If Jimmy serves and wins the first point, he has the advantage and the score is "ad-in." If John had won the point it would have been "ad-out." If Jimmy serves again while he is at ad-in and he wins another point, he is now ahead by 2 points and wins. But if John wins the point, they are back to deuce, and they continue playing until one of them is ahead by 2 points.

The first player to win six games wins the set. But as in a single game, so also in a set. In order to win you must be ahead by at least two games. So if Jimmy and John are tied at five games each, and John wins the next game and now has six games, he is not ahead by two games so they must keep playing. If Jimmy wins the next game, now they are knotted at six games apiece. In times past, they would continue until one player was ahead by two games. But recently they have begun to play a tiebreaker. This one game has at least 13 points. The first player to get 7 points wins the game and the match, as long as they are ahead by at least 2 points. For instance, if the score is 7-5, the game ends, but if it is 7-6, they keep playing until one player is ahead by at least 2 points. These games may continue until there is a score of 11-9, for example. But the set score is recorded as 7-6. In men's professional tennis, the first man to win three sets wins the match. In women's tennis, two sets wins the match.

Set	1	2	3	4	5
John McEnroe	6	6	6	6	4
Jimmy Conners	4	7	7	3	6

Jimmy Conners won the match because he won three sets. Notice that John McEnroe won more games 28–27, but lost the match since he won only two sets. Sets two and three were won in tiebreakers. If a player wins the first three sets he is said to have won in "straight sets."

Printing

As you read this book, think of the printer that produced it and the math that went into the process. We'll focus on three aspects in this lesson, but as with other lessons, much more could be written. In fact, as I spoke with Dave Cooper of Cooper Printing, he said the printing business is "all math."

Several areas beyond the scope of this lesson are percentages used in producing colors and decimals used on the computerized paper cutter. With four color tints, you can produce any color, just by changing the percentages. The four tints are cyan (bluish), magenta (reddish), yellow, and black. A color may contain 20% cyan, 35% magenta, 40% yellow, and 5% black. Each color will be a combination of the big four color tints. So if you specify "four color" to a printer for a job to be done, he knows he can produce any color you need.

PAPER SIZE

Some books have to be trimmed on the paper cutter. The paper cutter uses inches but not fractions. So all of the measurements are written as decimals. If you want to cut the length to 8½ inches you must enter it on the key pad as 8.500. Similarly, if you need 7⅜, that would be 7.375. The most common fractions are ½, ¼, ¾, ⅛, ⅜, ⅝, and ⅞, as well as 16ths and 32nds. Even though printers have access to conversion charts, it is helpful for estimation (and quicker) if they know the decimal equivalents in their heads. Color percents and cutter decimal fractions are two examples of math in printing, but the three topics I've chosen to focus on are paper size and weight, print size, and print layout, or signature.

If you are in the U.S., a "letter" size sheet of paper is measured in inches and is 8½" x 11". "Legal" size paper is 8 ½" x 14". You will also see 11" x 17", which is two 8½" x 11" pieces side by side, as in figure 1, and is referred to as "tabloid." There is also 5½" x 8½", which is half of 8½" x 11", as in figure 2.

Figure 1

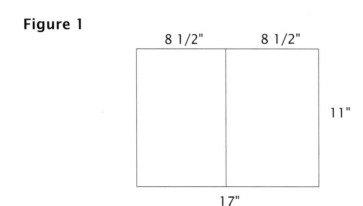

Figure 2

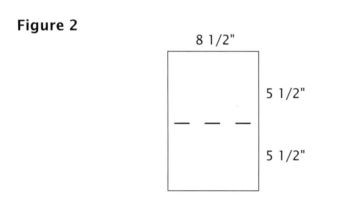

In countries that use metric, the standard size of a piece of paper is computed in millimeters. And while close to 8½" x 11", it is slightly different, and is referred to as A4. A4 paper is 210 mm x 297 mm or 8.26" x 11.69".

PAPER WEIGHT

Paper is also described by its weight. You will hear the expression in a print shop (or see it on the side of a package of paper) "20 pound bond." Bond means writing paper. When you hold it up to the light you see a watermark. The 20# or 24# refers to the weight of the paper. Paper is sold in reams, which are bundles of 500 sheets. A ream of 20# bond doesn't weigh 20 pounds, but a ream, or 500 sheets of 17" x 22", does. The "basic size" of paper is 17" x 22". You can see in figure 3 that this is four sheets of 8½" x 11". A ream of basic size 17" x 22" 24# bond weighs 24 pounds. A case of paper in an office supply store is 10 reams.

Figure 3

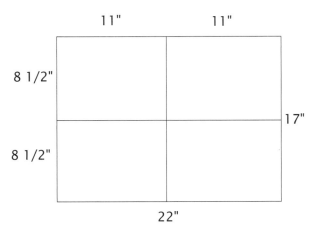

Offset paper is also used in printing. It has no watermark and comes in a different "basic size." The basic size of offset paper is 25" x 38". Five hundred sheets of 25" x 38" offset paper weigh 50 pounds. This kind of paper is called 50# offset. It is almost the same as 20# bond. Notice the different dimensions in the two basic sizes.

$$17" \times 22" = 374 \text{ in}^2 \text{ (bond)}$$
$$25" \times 38" = 950 \text{ in}^2 \text{ (offset)}$$

When I divide 374 into 950 I get 2.54. So I find that the offset is almost two and a half times as many square inches as the bond. So it should weigh two and a half times as much. And 20# times 2.5 equals 50#. So even though 20# and 50# don't seem to be the same weight, the amount of change in the area affects the final weight! 20# bond and 50# offset are virtually the same paper. Likewise, 24# bond corresponds to 60# offset.

PAPER BRIGHTNESS

If you are purchasing paper for your own use, consider the weight (20# or 24#), the price (obviously), and the brightness. According to Dave, our printer, this runs in cycles. If you want a brighter paper, look for the higher number on the package. You will find 20# 96 U.S. bright, 20# 92 bright, and 20# 84 bright, to name a few. 96 is "brighter" than 84, and more expensive.

FONT SIZE

You will encounter two other words in the printing industry, points and picas, that are used in measuring fonts (types or letter styles) and line spacing. A common font, or type style, is Times 12, which means the font Times with a size of 12 points. There are 12 points in a pica and six picas in one inch. Putting these together we find 72 points per inch. A letter 12 points high is one pica, or $^{12}/_{72}$" or ⅙ of an inch high. How high would a ½ inch letter be in points? ½ inch = $^{36}/_{72}$, so 36 points or three picas. A piece of paper with ½ inch margins at the top and bottom would have a 10½" writing surface, which is 10½" times 72 points per inch, or 756 points vertically. You can see how a typesetter would be very familiar with font size and line spacing.

LAYOUT

Once a book has been typeset and the size of the paper in the book chosen, it is now time to lay it out for the printing machine. Each printed piece of paper is called a signature.

Since offset paper comes in various sizes, this signature will be different from book to book, but let's say we have 23" x 35" paper. How many signatures can we put on a piece if each of them is 8½" x 14" (legal size)?

Figure 4

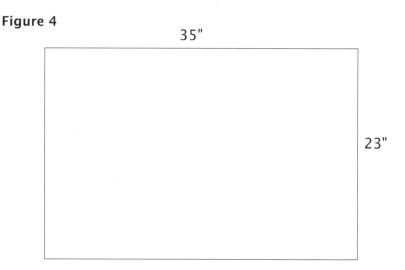

35"

23"

Figure 5
Legal Size

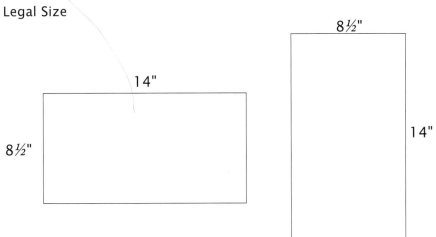

14"

8½"

8½"

14"

Figure 6

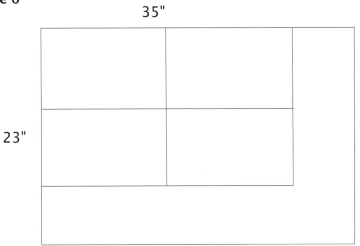

35"

23"

If you lay them out horizontally, you can get four signatures out of a basic size.

Figure 7

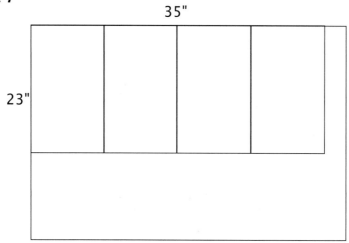

35"

23"

If they run vertically you get four signatures out of a basic size as well.

Figure 8

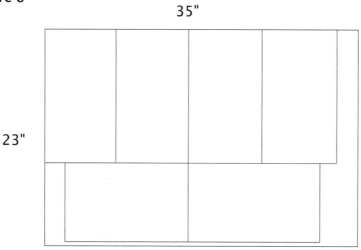

35"

23"

But if you lay them out horizontally and vertically, you have six signatures per sheet of paper, which is the most efficient use of the space. Remember the words of Dave Cooper, printing is "all math"!

LESSON 28

GPA and Wind Chill

GRADE POINT AVERAGE

There are two factors that contribute to computing a GPA or grade point average: the grade and the number of credits. It is also referred to as the QPA or quality point average. While some colleges differ on the value of a credit, generally it is the number of classroom hours the class meets per week. A three-credit course, the most common, might meet M, W, F from 9 to 10 a.m., or T, Th from 1 to 2:30 p.m. Either way, you are in a classroom three hours per week. The grades are A, B, C, D, and F. The numerical equivalents are A—4, B—3, C—2, D—1, F—0. If you see a 4.0 GPA, that means a student has all As or straight As.

Example 1

Course	% Grade	Letter Grade	Credit	Calculation	GPA
English	84	B	3	3 x 3 = 9	
Algebra	98	A	3	3 x 4 = 12	
Science	85	B	3	3 x 3 = 9	
History	81	B	3	3 x 3 = 9	
Latin	93	A	3	3 x 4 = 12	
Phys. Ed.	88	B	1	1 x 3 = 3	
			16	54	3.38

Grade points are grades times credits. In the English course, a B is 3 points so you multiply that by the number of credits, which is 3, to get 9. To find the GPA, divide the total grade points in the calculation column by the total number of credits. 54 ÷ 16 = 3.375, which is rounded to 3.38.

QUALITY POINT AVERAGE

Some schools grade using pluses and minuses. Instead of just an A, you can get an A, an A+, and an A−. These have number equivalents as well and are shown in figure 1.

Figure 1

A+ 4.3	**B+** 3.3	**C+** 2.3	**D+** 1.3
A 4.0	**B** 3.0	**C** 2.0	**D** 1.0
A− 3.7	**B−** 2.7	**C−** 1.7	**D−** 0.7

In example 2, the QPA is computed using pluses and minuses. The breakdown for what qualifies as an A+ or an A− may vary from school to school and professor to professor. I have chosen the following standard for this report card. 97 to 100 is an A+, 93 to 96 is an A, and 90 to 92 is an A−. 87 to 89 is a B+, 83 to 86 is a B, and 80 to 82 is a B−. The same numbers will apply to the other letter scores. You will see that the same grades produce different GPAs depending on which method you use to compute the scores.

Example 2

Course	Percentage Grade	Letter Grade	Credit	Calculation
English	84	B	3	3 x 3.0 = 9.0
Algebra	98	A+	3	3 x 4.3 = 12.9
Science	85	B	3	3 x 3.0 = 9.0
History	81	B−	3	3 x 2.7 = 8.1
Latin	93	A−	3	3 x 3.7 = 11.1
Phys. Ed.	88	B+	1	1 x 3.3 = 3.3
			16	53.4

QPA = 3.3375 ≈ 3.34

WIND CHILL FACTOR

Have you ever noticed that some days feel colder than others even though the temperature is the same? If the temperature is 60° F and it is a calm, sunny day, it is comfortable. But if you have a gusty wind, it can feel colder. This change in temperature is called the wind chill factor, and we are going to see how to figure it.

Wind chill makes the air seem colder than it really is because the wind carries heat away from the body. If there is no wind, the heat radiating from your body stays around you like a layer of clothing, but wind will blow this covering away, and the more wind, the more "felt" heat loss. In the chart below there are rounded figures that help us figure heat loss. The formula used in computing them is intricate and not something you can do in your head. The U.S. National Weather Service uses this formula for calculating wind chill. Here it is:

$$WC = 91.4 - (.474677 - .020425 \cdot V + .303107 \cdot \sqrt{V})(91.4 - T)$$

Velocity

	0	5	10	15	20	25
40°	40°	37°	28°	22°	18°	15°
30°	30°	27°	16°	9°	4°	1°
20°	20°	16°	4°	–4°	–10°	–14°
10°	10°	6°	–9°	–18°	–24°	–29°
0°	0°	–5°	–21°	–31°	–39°	–44°

Temperature labels the rows on the left.

Example 3
Find the wind chill for a temperature of 30° and a wind speed, or velocity, of 25 mph. Can you find this on the chart?

$$WC = 91.4 - (.474677 - .020425 \cdot V + .303107 \cdot \sqrt{V})(91.4 - T)$$

$$WC = 91.4 - (.474677 - .020425 \cdot 25 + .303107 \cdot \sqrt{25})(91.4 - 30)$$

$$WC = 91.4 - (.474677 - .510625 + .303107 \cdot 5)(61.4)$$

$$WC = 91.4 - (.474677 - .510625 + 1.515535)(61.4)$$

$$WC = 91.4 - (1.479587)(61.4)$$

$$WC = 91.4 - 90.8466418$$

$$WC = .5533582, \text{ which is rounded to } 1°$$

STEWARDSHIP

Air, Train, Bus, or Car

Let's say you're planning to take a ten-day trip to Florida. Aside from your ticket or fare, you will have other expenses to take into consideration. If you are flying, taking a train, or riding a bus, you'll need a rental car once you arrive, which you won't need if you are driving. When this was written, a full-sized vehicle, including taxes, was about $180.00 for a week, plus the few additional days at $40.00 each day. If you fly you'll need the car for 10 days, since you can get there in only a few hours. When you travel by train or bus, you are in transit one day each way, so you need the car for only eight days.

Air   To get air fares I usually begin with an online travel service like Travelocity, Orbitz, or Expedia. You are given a lot of information about which airlines fly to which destinations, plus the different fares. Not every airline is listed on these sites. Because these travel services charge a fee for listing the airlines and their information, the discount airlines won't be listed. To fly from Baltimore to Tampa, Expedia tells me I can fly at fares beginning at $132.00 round trip, per person. I then visit the Southwest Airlines web site, which is not listed on the larger travel sites. The price to fly Southwest is $118.40. So we'll round the airfare to $125.00 per person. It used to be that to get a decent fare, you had to stay over a Saturday night, say, leaving on a Friday and returning on a Monday. That is no longer the case. But length of time in advance is a factor. The later you wait to buy your tickets, the more you will spend. Give yourself at least seven days for advance booking and preferably 14 or 21 days. Most airlines charge a fee for changing a flight reservation, but there are some like Southwest who do not. This fee can be $50.00, $75.00, or even $100.00 per ticket. In this lesson we will compare four ways of traveling: air, train, bus, and car. To make it a real situation, I chose to have us take a trip from Baltimore, Maryland, to Tampa, Florida, and to have 10 days set aside for the trip. The distance is around 1,000 miles. There are several factors to consider: expense, time, comfort, and number of people traveling. I have found AAA (American Automobile Association) to be a good resource for any kind of travel. You can learn more about it at AAA.com.

Train   Amtrak is $87.00 each way or $174.00 for a round trip.

Bus   Greyhound is $118.00 for a round trip with a seven-day advance purchase.

Car   This is a little more complicated, but we'll look at just the price of operating a vehicle for a 1,000-mile journey. 1,000 x 30¢ per mile = $300.00. Round trip makes $600.00. Gas itself is 20 mpg or 50 gallons each way x $2.00* per gallon = $100.00 each way or $200.00 round trip.

Another charge when driving is staying at a hotel, unless you drive straight through. For this exercise, let's say we did that on the way home. Figure a hotel for $75.00. If we put all of these costs on a chart it looks like figure 1.

* The price of fuel has fluctuated since I first wrote this book in 2005. Fuel charges affect the cost of driving as well as all other forms of transportation. When you plan a real trip, check all of the data with the rates at that time. The prices given here will suffice to illustrate the principles.

TIME

Air   The flight is 2 hours and 20 minutes, plus getting to and from the airport.

Train   The ride is 21 hours and 32 minutes, plus getting to and from the station.

Bus   The ride is 23 hours, plus getting to and from terminal.

Car   The ride is 17–19 hours, depending on how fast you drive and how many pit stops you make.

Figure 1

1 Traveler	Price	Rental Car	Hotel	Total
Air	125	380		505
Train	174	300		474
Bus	118	300		418
Car	600		75	675

2 Travelers	Price	Rental Car	Hotel	Total
Air	250	380		630
Train	348	300		648
Bus	236	300		536
Car	600		75	675

4 Travelers	Price	Rental Car	Hotel	Total
Air	500	380		880
Train	696	300		996
Bus	472	300		772
Car	600		75	675

COMFORT

This is your call, but it does seem that air wins in this category.

NUMBER OF PEOPLE TRAVELING

For air, train, and bus, the fares are per person, with a few discounts for children. Driving a car allows for four people to travel at virtually the same price as one person. The charts on the previous page reflect the prices for different numbers of travelers.

There is no one best way to travel, but I hope this study has helped you to think through some of the issues and plan accordingly. Technology is changing so rapidly that by the time this book is printed there may be other resources to help you make your decision.

Some of you may be thinking about priceline.com and some of its discount airfares. I only tried them once and had to eat four tickets. I had bid on the price and was somewhat flexible on my travel dates so I did receive good fares at decent times. But then I had to attend a funeral and there is no budge with this travel service. So I lost the price of four tickets. I tell you this so you'll know two things: (1) there are many options out there, so research carefully; and (2) everything has a price tag. I took a chance and made the reservations, but one of the reasons for the low fares is the lack of flexibility. I therefore lost on my attempt to save a few bucks. So be careful with the great deals. If it seems too good to be true, it probably is.

Prayer, careful planning, and research will win the day!

MILEAGE CHART

The mileage chart on the following page provides you with a tool to find the distance between cities in the U.S. and Canada. There are charts with more and less detail and information. To read this chart, notice that the same cities along the left edge are also across the top. To find the mileage between two cities, consult the chart and find one city down the left column, then go across that row until it intersects the column of the city across the top of the page. You may use the cities in either order as each distance is on the map two times.

	Atlanta	Boston	Calgary	Chicago	Dallas	Denver	Miami	New Orleans	Pittsburgh	St. Louis	Sacramento	Seattle
Atlanta	- - -	1,092	2,415	716	811	1,439	667	484	688	562	2,561	2,734
Boston	1,092	- - -	2,560	976	1,794	1,969	1,498	1,537	590	1,185	3,042	3,041
Calgary	2,415	2,560	- - -	1,699	2,150	1,158	3,082	2,603	2,168	1,912	1,475	682
Chicago	716	976	1,699	- - -	993	1,012	1,383	1,007	469	304	2,085	2,065
Dallas	811	1,794	2,150	993	- - -	901	1,393	554	1,254	640	1,868	2,238
Denver	1,439	1,969	1,158	1,012	901	- - -	2,106	1,446	1,462	879	1,212	1,343
Miami	667	1,498	3,082	1,383	1,393	2,106	- - -	871	1,180	1,229	3,217	3,401
New Orleans	484	1,537	2,603	1,007	554	1,446	871	- - -	1,110	690	2,378	2,783
Pittsburgh	688	590	2,168	469	1,254	1,462	1,180	1,110	- - -	612	2,533	2,532
St. Louis	562	1,185	1,912	304	640	879	1,229	690	612	- - -	2,038	2,174
Sacramento	2,561	3,042	1,475	2,085	1,868	1,212	3,217	2,378	2,533	2,038	- - -	793
Seattle	2,734	3,041	682	2,065	2,238	1,343	3,401	2,783	2,532	2,174	793	- - -

Example 1
Find the distance between Pittsburgh and Denver.

I can look down the left column until I find Pittsburgh. Then reading across the columns, I find the vertical one that corresponds to Denver. At the intersection of these two cities, I read 1,462 miles.

Or, I read down the left to Denver, then move to the right until I find the Pittsburgh column, then read the same distance at the intersection, 1,462 miles.

USPS or UPS

SHIPPING

One of the key principles in comparison shopping is to make sure you are comparing apples to apples. Two of the most common ways to ship a package are via USPS and UPS. USPS stands for United States Postal Service, and UPS is the United Parcel Service. The color theme of USPS is red, white, and blue, while the color of UPS is brown.

I compared the cost of shipping two packages with the dimensions 12" x 12" x 12". The first package weighs 5# and the second weighs 25#. The value of each package is $100.00. I randomly chose to ship them from Drumore, Pennsylvania, to Moore, Oklahoma. There are advantages with both services, but I will mention these after the final chart.

There are three options with USPS: Express Mail, which is overnight to most areas; Priority Mail, which is marketed as two days but is not guaranteed; and Parcel Post, which will take at least six days.

There are four options with UPS, as you can see in figure 1. The big difference is that UPS guarantees that the package will be there in the time stated for first couple categories and is pretty reliable even for ground shipping. So we are not really comparing apples to apples. Also, tracking numbers are a part of UPS, and there is no additional fee for this service. Insurance is free up to $100.00, then there is a charge of $1.00 per $100.00 value after that.

Figure 1

USPS 5 lb package	Price	Tracking #	Insurance	Total
Express Mail	$27.30	$.45	$2.20	$29.95
Priority mail	$9.85	$.45	$2.20	$12.50
Parcel Post	$8.58	$.55	$2.20	$11.33

UPS 5 lb package	Price	Tracking #	Insurance	Total
Next Day Guarantee	$64.33	free	free	$64.33
2nd Day Guarantee	$38.93	free	free	$38.93
3 Day Select	$25.79	free	free	$25.79
Ground, 4 Days	$10.10	free	free	$10.10

Here are some additional observations from someone who does a lot of shipping. One of the perks for USPS is that there are many post offices, which is a definite convenience. Also, while the 2nd Day Air is guaranteed for UPS, it is more expensive than even Express Mail for USPS, and definitely more than Priority Mail, which may make it in two days. Express Mail in USPS is more like 2nd Day Air with UPS because it is not guaranteed to be there the next day. I have used the Express Mail, but since I live in a rural area, it took two days to get to its destination. Other times I have sent a package with Priority Mail and it did get there in two days. So it is hit or miss with USPS but reliable with UPS, at least in the U.S. When I did this comparison, the rate for UPS was computed as if you were shipping from a UPS retail store. If you have a UPS account out of your home or place of business, shipping will be cheaper.

As a shipper I use both services, as there are positives with both USPS and UPS.

Understanding all of the options and comparing apples to apples helps me make informed decisions. If you are interested in finding costs yourself, both services have excellent web sites: www.UPS.com and www.USPS.com.

Figure 2

USPS 25 lb package	Price	Tracking #	Insurance	Total
Express Mail	$60.65	$.45	$2.20	$63.30
Priority mail	$31.10	$.45	$2.20	$33.75
Parcel Post	$19.22	$.55	$2.20	$21.97

UPS 25 lb package	Price	Tracking #	Insurance	Total
Next Day Guarantee	$106.22	free	free	$106.22
2nd Day Guarantee	$82.18	free	free	$82.18
3 Day Select	$50.42	free	free	$50.42
Ground, 4 Days	$21.11	free	free	$21.11

The most common shipping methods are USPS parcel post and UPS ground. When you compare $21.97 (six or more days) and $21.11 (four days), and factor in the extra days to get there, I think UPS wins. But do your own homework and consider all of the factors when making your decision.

DIRECTION AND POINTS ON A COMPASS

While there are four main directions—north, east, south, and west—there are also more specific directions. If you are traveling in a direction halfway between north and east, you are said to be going northeast. Halfway between south and west is southwest. These directions have numerical equivalents on a circle in the form of degrees. In geometry we begin at 0°, which would be east. When using direction, north is 0°. Since a circle has 360°, each of the four main directions is 90°. If north, or 0° is where we start, east is 90°, south is 180°, and west is 270°. Northeast would be between east (90°) and north (0°) or 45°. The others follow the same pattern. See a visual example of this on the following page.

There are also more specific directions like ENE, which is between east and northeast, and SSW, which is between south and southwest. The degree equivalent between north and NNE is 22.5°. Since NNE is between northeast, 45°, and east, 90°, it is 67.5° on the compass.

Figure 3

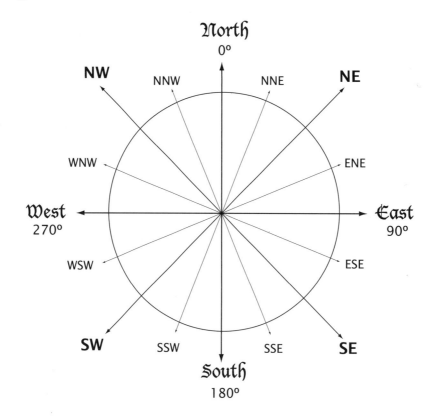

Student Solutions 𝕂

Lesson Practice 1.1

1. 34 × 6.00 = $204.00

2. Time and a half is 6.00 x 1.5 = $9.00
   (40 x 6.00) + (3.5 x 9.00) = $271.50

3. Time and a half is 6.00 x 1.5 = $9.00
   (40 x 6.00) + (7 x 9.00) = $303.00

4. 34 + 43.5 + 47 = 124.5
   204.00 + 271.50 + 303.00 = $778.50
   $778.50 ÷ 124.5 = $6.25

5. 11.75 x 2,000 = $23,500

6. 27,000 ÷ 2,000 = $13.50

7. 79,500 x .03 = $2,385.00

8. .11 x 100 x 8 = $88.00
   $88.00 ÷ 6 = $14.67

9. 25 x 1.25 = $31.25
   31.25 ÷ 2.75 = $11.36

10. Answers may vary.

    by the hour - You can count on getting
    a certain amount no matter how much
    work is accomplished.

    by the piece - If you work faster, you
    can earn more.

Lesson Practice 1.2

1. 10.75 x 38.5 = $413.88

2. Time and a half is 10.75 x 1.5 = 16.13
   (40 x 10.75) + (11 x 16.13) = $607.43

3. Time and a half is 10.75 x 1.5 = 16.13
   (40 x 10.75) + (8.25 x 16.13) =
   $563.07

4. 38.5 + 51 + 48.25 = 137.75
   413.88 + 607.43 + 563.07 =$1,584.38
   1,584.38 ÷ 137.75 = $11.50

5. 18.33 x 2,000 = $36,660

6. 44,500 ÷ 2,000 = $22.25

7. 112,000 x .06 = $6,720.00

8. .60 x 47 = $28.20
   28.20 ÷ 3.25 = $8.68

9. 83 x .45 = $37.35
   37.35 ÷ 3.5 = $10.67

10. Answers may vary.

    Hourly wages mean a regular paycheck,
    easier to budget.

    A commission rewards extra effort
    or skill.

Lesson Review 1.3

1. (7.50) x 25 = $187.50

2. 7.50 x 2.5 = $11.25 time and a half
   (40 x 7.5) + (1 x 11.25) = $311.25

3. (8.25 x 40 x 50) = $16,500.00 if we
   assume a 50 week work year

4. $52,500.00 ÷ 2000 = $26.25

5. .15 x 950 = $142.50

6. Bereans, Acts 17:11

7. 1 John 5:14-15, Luke 11:9,
   James 4:2-3

8. "according to his will" 1 John 5:14-15

9. God, Psalm 50:10

10. Answers may vary: someone who takes
    care of what belongs to someone else

Lesson Review 1.4

1. 9.25 x 38 = $351.50

2. $9.25 x 1.5 = $13.88 (rounded)
    (9.25 x 40) + (13.88 x 8) =
    370 + 111.04 = $481.04

3. 20 x 2000 = $40,000.00

4. 75,000.00 ÷ 2000 = $37.50

5. 375 x .20 = $75.00

6. Blessed

7. Proverbs 8:22-32

8. When he prepared the heavens,
    Jesus was there: When he set a
    compass upon the face of the depth
    Proverbs 8:27

    Then Jesus was by him, as one brought
    up with him; and Jesus was daily his
    delight, Rejoicing always before him,
    Proverbs 8:30

9. faithfulness

10. and upon the earth beneath

Lesson Practice 2.1

1. 37.25 x .15 = $5.59

2. 37.25 x .05 = $1.86

3. 37.25 + 5.59 + 1.86 = $44.70
    Add 30¢ (or $.30), since
    44.70 + .30 = $45.00

4. 26.95 x .15 = $4.04

5. More than $4.04, probably $5.00
    or $6.00

6. 26.95 x .05 = $1.35

7. 26.95 + 4.04 + 1.35 = $32.34
    .66 to make it 33.00
    1.66 to make it 34.00

8. 874.50 - 8.75 (rounded) = $865.75

9. Yes, I should. 1,358 x .02 = $27.16

10. 573.92 x .05 = $28.70
    573.92 - 28.70 = $545.22

11. 573.92 x .01 = $5.74
    573.92 + 5.74 = 579.66

Lesson Practice 2.2

1. 76.85 x .16 = $12.30

2. 76.85 x .0675 = $5.19

3. 76.85 + 12.30 + 5.19 = $94.34
    Answers may vary. $94.00 or $95.00

4. 93.20 x .15 = $13.98

5. This will vary, between $10.00
    and $13.00

6. 93.20 x .0725 = $6.76

7. 93.20 + 6.76 = $99.96
    Add $12.04 to make it $112.00
    (this may vary)

8. $1,299.00

9. $265.00 - full amount

10. 1,002.73 x .02 = 20.05
    1,002.73 - 20.05 = $982.68

11. $1,002.73

Lesson Review 2.3

1. 29.60 x .16 = $4.74

2. 29.60 x .06 = $1.78

3. $1,075.00

4. 573.92 x .05 = $28.70

5. 573.92 x .01 = $5.74

6. (12 x 100) x .15 = $180.00,
    $180.00 ÷ 15 = $12.00

7. 54 x 1.05 = $56.70
    56.70 ÷ 4 = $14.18

8. no, the love of money is, 1 Tim 6:10

9. heart, soul, mind, strength

10. No, Luke 16:13

Lesson Review 2.4

1. 9.50 x 4 = $38.00

2. Tax = $2.47, tip = $1.90,
   38.00 + 2.47 + 1.90 = $42.37

3. 2,857 x .02 = $57.14

4. 1,002 x .02 = $20.05

5. $1,002.73

6. 1.25 x 42 = $52.50,
   52.5 ÷ 4 = $13.13

7. 103 x .60 = $61.80,
   61.80 ÷ 5 = $12.36

8. Anything we look to in order to supply what only God can provide.

9. Lovers of money

10. He had great possessions.

Lesson Practice 3.1

1. 22,800 ÷ 26 = $876.92
   Paycheck $876.92
   Federal Withholding .... $ 74.54
   State .... $ 26.92
   County .... $ 14.47
   FICA .... $ 54.37
   FICA .... $ 12.72
   SUI .... $.79
   Total $183.81

2. Federal Withholding

3. SUI

4. FUTA .... $ 7.02
   FICA .... $ 54.37
   FICA .... $ 12.72
   SUI .... $ 18.17
   Total $92.28

5. 78,000.00 x .03 = $2,340.00
   $2,340.00 x 50 = $117,000.00 yearly
   117,000.00 ÷ 50 = $2,340.00 weekly

6.
   Paycheck $2,340.00
   Federal Withholding .. $ 280.80
   State .... $ 71.84
   County .... $ 38.61
   FICA .... $ 145.08
   FICA .... $ 33.93
   SUI .... $ 2.11
   Total $572.37

   2,340.00 – 572.37 = $1,767.63

7. $176.76

Lesson Practice 3.2

1. Paycheck

   485 x .11 x 100 = $5,335.00

2. Federal Withholding .. $ 106.70
   State .... $ 163.78
   County .... $ 88.03
   FICA .... $ 330.77
   FICA .... $ 77.36
   SUI .... $ 4.80
   Total $771.44

3. 40 x 17.75 = $710.00

4. (5)(17.75)(1.5) = $133.13
   710.00 + 133.13 = $843.13

5. Paycheck $843.13
   Federal Withholding .... $ 75.88
   State .... $ 25.88
   County .... $ 13.91
   FICA .... $ 52.27
   FICA .... $ 12.23
   SUI .... $.76
   Total $180.93

   843.13 – 180.93 = $662.20

6. FUTA .... $ 6.75
   FICA .... $ 52.27
   FICA .... $ 12.23
   SUI .... $ 17.47
   Total $88.72

7. $84.31

Lesson Review 3.3

1 $43,500.00 divided by 26 = $1,673.08

Federal Withholding ... $142.21
State .... $ 51.36
County .... $ 27.61
FICA .... $ 103.73
FICA .... $ 24.26
SUI .... $ 1.51
Total $350.68

2. 8.5
3.07
1.65
6.2
1.45
+ .09
20.96%

3. 1673.08 – 350.68 = $1,322.40

4. FUTA .... $ 13.38
FICA .... $ 103.73
FICA .... $ 24.26
SUI .... $ 34.67
Total $176.04

5. 1322.40 x .10 = $132.24

6. $51.65, $3.15 tax

7. .18 x 48.50 = $8.73

51.65 + 8.73 = $60.38, so $61.00

8. Thou shalt not kill. Thou shalt

not steal. Exodus 20:13, 15

9. loving

10. And one of them, a lawyer, asked him a question, trying him: 'Teacher, which is the great commandment in the law?'

And he said unto him, **Thou shalt love the Lord thy God with all thy heart, and with all thy soul, and with all thy mind.** This is the great and first commandment. And a second like unto it is this, Thou shalt **love thy neighbor as thyself.** *Matthew 22:37-40 ASV*

Lesson Review 3.4

1. 125 x 40 x .65 = $3,250

2. Federal
Withholding............... $ 65.00
State .... $ 99.78
County .... $ 53.63
FICA .... $ 201.50
FICA .... $ 47.13
SUI .... $ 2.93
Total $469.97

3. 38 x 15.25 = $579.50

4. 579.50 x 16 = $9272.00

5. 579.50 x .10 = $57.95

6. 37.75 + 1.89 = $39.64

7. 37.75 x .16 = 6.04
they saved $6.04

8. gave

9. unselfishly giving

10. polar opposites

Lesson Practice 4.1

1. Any 2 of the following answers would be correct: Checking, Savings, Loans, ATM

2. members of the community

3. fees

4. maintain a larger balance in your account

5. security, trust, fidelity

6. mortgage

7. Automated Teller Machine

8. Answers may vary.

9. $Wp \times 300 = 1.50$

$Wp \times \dfrac{300}{300} = \dfrac{1.50}{300.00}$

$Wp \times \dfrac{300}{300} = \dfrac{1.50}{300.00}$

$Wp \times \dfrac{1.50}{300.00} = .005 = .5\%$ or $1/2\%$

10. Answers may vary.

Lesson Practice 4.2

1. any two answers not given on the last page: Checking, Savings, Loans, ATM

2. a bank

3. lending and receiving interest

4. The bank should be paid for the work they do for you.

5. a written record of a savings account

6. money that you have paid down on your mortgage

7. an ATM card

8. an account at your bank to save money

9. $Wp \times 150 = 2$

$Wp \times \dfrac{150}{150} = \dfrac{2}{150}$

$Wp = \dfrac{2}{150} = .0133 = 1.33\%$

10. usually nothing

Lesson Review 4.3

1. Answers may vary.

2. Answers may vary.

3. Answers may vary.

4. Answers may vary.

5. 6 x 875 = $5,250
   5250 x 12 = $63,000
   63,000/50 = $1,260

6. Federal Withholding ... $151.20
   State $38.68
   County $20.79
   FICA $78.12
   FICA $18.27
   SUI $1.13
   Total $308.19

   1260.00 – 308.19 = $951.81

7. $95.18

8. Answers may vary.

9. Proverbs 30:8b-9

10. Answers may vary.

Lesson Review 4.4

1. Answers may vary.

2. Answers may vary.

3. Answers may vary.

4. Answers may vary.

5. Federal Withholding ... $ 55.00
   State .... $ 84.43
   County .... $ 45.38
   FICA .... $ 170.50
   FICA .... $ 39.88
   SUI .... $ 2.48
   Total $397.67

6. FUTA .... $ 22.00
   FICA .... $ 170.50
   FICA .... $ 39.88
   SUI .... $ 56.98
   Total $289.36

7. 2750.00 – 397.67 = 2352.33
   2352.33÷14 = $168.02/wk
   168.02 x .10 = $16.80

8. I know how to be **abased,** and I know also how to **abound:** in everything and in all things have I learned the secret both to be filled and to be **hungry,** both to abound and to be in want. ASV

9. great gain, 1 Timothy 6:6

10. Answers may vary.

Lesson Practice 5.1

1. Joseph B. Unit

2. Manny Tens

3. 125.00 in the box,
One hundred twenty-five and 00/100 on the line

4. 1556

5. See figure 1 on the next page.

6.

7.

8. See figure 2 on the next page.

9.

BALANCE THIS STATEMENT		$ 550	40
Add			
Deposits made since this statement		$ —	0
SUBTOTAL		$ 550	40
Checks issued but not on the statement			
Number	Amount		
478	$	60	00
479	$	34	75
TOTAL OUTSTANDING CHECKS		$ 94	75
CURRENT BALANCE		$ 455	65

Lesson Practice 5.2

1. 07893456

2. middle number below memo line under address, different sequence

3. 12 Main St., Goodtown, PA 15000

4. to state the purpose of a check

5. See figure 3 on the next page.

6.

7.

STEWARDSHIP

Figure 1

NEIGHBORS BANK
12 Main Street
Goodtown, PA 15000
12-3456/789

1557

Joseph B. Unit
369 Decimal Street
Place Value, PA 01234

DATE July 12, 2005 — Date will vary.

PAY TO THE ORDER OF Jack Taylor $ 279.00

Two-hundred seventy-nine and 00/100 DOLLARS

MEMO Guitar payment

Joseph B. Unit
AUTHORIZED SIGNATURE

⑈ 001557⑈ ⑆07893456⑆ 08⑈ 987654⑈ 02

Figure 2

■ AD-Automatic Deposit ■ AP-Automatic Payment ■ ATM-Teller Machine ■ DC-Debit Card ■ T-Tax Deductible ■ TT-Telephone Transfer

NUMBER OR CODE	DATE	TRANSACTION DESCRIPTION	PAYMENT AMOUNT		✓	FEE	DEPOSIT AMOUNT		$ 305	.40
475	5/20	Guitar lesson	$ 25	00	✓		$		280	40
476	5/25	Swimming Class	15	00	✓				265	40
	5/27	Deposited Paycheck			✓		360	00	625	40
477	5/27	Focus on the Family	50	00	✓				575	40
478	6/13	Car Insurance	60	00					515	40
479	6/15	Cell Phone	34	75					480	65
480	6/18	Cash	25	00	✓				455	65

Figure 3

NEIGHBORS BANK
12 Main Street
Goodtown, PA 15000
12-3456/789

1557

Joseph B. Unit
369 Decimal Street
Place Value, PA 01234

DATE July 12, 2005 — Date will vary.

PAY TO THE ORDER OF Ricky Ricardo $ 1,595.84

One thousand five hundred ninety-five and 84/100 DOLLARS

MEMO Bongo Drums

Joseph B. Unit
AUTHORIZED SIGNATURE

⑈ 001557⑈ ⑆07893456⑆ 08⑈ 987654⑈ 02

8. See figure 4 on the next page.
9.

BALANCE THIS STATEMENT	$ 638|99
Add Deposits made since this statement	$ 178|21
SUBTOTAL	$ 817|20

Checks issued but not on the statement

Number	Amount		
483	$	36	00
485	$	8	55
TOTAL OUTSTANDING CHECKS	$	44	55
CURRENT BALANCE	$	772	65

Lesson Review 5.3

1. See figure 5 on the next page.
2. no, checks 204, 207, and a deposit haven't cleared.
3-4. yes

BALANCE THIS STATEMENT	$ 327|25
Add Deposits made since this statement	$ 125|76
SUBTOTAL	$ 453|01

Checks issued but not on the statement

Number	Amount		
204	$	75	00
207	$	50	00
TOTAL OUTSTANDING CHECKS	$	125	00
CURRENT BALANCE	$	328	01

5. Answers may vary.
6. Answers may vary.
7. Federal Insurance Contribution Act
8. His inner man, the essence of a man
9. David
10. As you believe in your heart, your life is transformed from within.

Believe in your heart
Romans 10:8-10

Heart ultimately makes our decisions
Proverbs 4:23

Out of the heart the mouth speaks
Matthew 12:34

Connected to our treasure **Luke 12:34**

Lesson Review 5.4

1. See figure 6 on the next page.
2. no, 2 checks haven't cleared, 359 and 360.
3-4. yes

BALANCE THIS STATEMENT	$ 797|30
Add Deposits made since this statement	$
SUBTOTAL	$ 797|30

Checks issued but not on the statement

Number	Amount		
359	$	18	70
360	$	40	00
TOTAL OUTSTANDING CHECKS	$	58	70
CURRENT BALANCE	$	738	60

5. Answers may vary.
6. Answers may vary.
7. Answers may vary.
8. What you spend your money on is a good indicator of what you think is important. Luke 12:34
9. Ezekiel 36:26
10. Luke 12:34, 1-2-3-4

Lesson Practice 6.1

1. 500 x .06 = $30.00

Figure 4

■ AD-Automatic Deposit	■ AP-Automatic Payment	■ ATM-Teller Machine	■ DC-Debit Card	■ T-Tax Deductible	■ TT-Telephone Transfer				

NUMBER OR CODE	DATE	TRANSACTION DESCRIPTION	PAYMENT AMOUNT		✓	FEE	DEPOSIT AMOUNT		$ BALANCE	
481	6/20	Barnes & Noble	$ 69	96	✓		$		385	69
482	6/25	Radio Shack	102	50	✓				283	19
	6/27	Deposited Paycheck			✓		360	00	643	19
483	6/27	Calvary Church	36	00					607	19
484	7/13	Library Fees	4	20	✓				602	99
485	7/15	Video Rental	8	55					594	44
	7/19	Deposited Tax Refund					178	21	772	65

Figure 5

■ AD-Automatic Deposit	■ AP-Automatic Payment	■ ATM-Teller Machine	■ DC-Debit Card	■ T-Tax Deductible	■ TT-Telephone Transfer				

NUMBER OR CODE	DATE	TRANSACTION DESCRIPTION	PAYMENT AMOUNT		✓	FEE	DEPOSIT AMOUNT		$ BALANCE	
203	3/07	Computer Software	$ 45	00	✓		$		219	70
204	3/10	Singing Lessons	75	00					144	70
	3/10	Deposited Birthday Check			✓		240	00	384	70
205	3/12	Joni & Friends	100	00	✓				284	70
206	3/19	Flowers for Morris Birthday	32	45	✓				252	25
207	3/27	Cash	50	00					202	25
	3/31	Deposited Tax Refund					125	76	328	01

Figure 6

■ AD-Automatic Deposit	■ AP-Automatic Payment	■ ATM-Teller Machine	■ DC-Debit Card	■ T-Tax Deductible	■ TT-Telephone Transfer				

NUMBER OR CODE	DATE	TRANSACTION DESCRIPTION	PAYMENT AMOUNT		✓	FEE	DEPOSIT AMOUNT		$ BALANCE	
356	8/01	Strasburg Mini-Golf	$ 17	50	✓		$		423	75
357	8/05	Circuit City	53	95	✓				369	80
	8/08	Deposited Paycheck			✓		475	00	844	80
358	8/10	First Community Church	47	50	✓				797	30
359	8/24	Goodwill	18	70					778	60
360	8/25	Wawa Gas Station	40	00					738	60

2. 6% ÷ 4 = 1.5% per quarter

Quarter	Principal	Interest (1.5%)	New Balance
1	500.00	7.50	507.50
2	507.50	7.61	515.11
3	515.11	7.73	522.84
4	522.84	7.84	530.68

may be slightly different answer due to rounding

3. 6% ÷ 12 = .5% per month

Month	Principal	Interest (.5%)	New Balance
1	500.00	2.50	502.50
2	502.50	2.51	505.01
3	505.01	2.53	507.54
4	507.54	2.54	510.08
5	510.08	2.55	512.63
6	512.63	2.56	515.19
7	515.19	2.58	517.77
8	517.77	2.59	520.36
9	520.36	2.60	522.96
10	522.96	2.61	525.57
11	525.57	2.63	528.20
12	528.20	2.64	530.84

4. WP = what percent
530.84 − 500.00 = 30.84
WP of 500.00 = 30.84
WP = 30.84 / 500.00
WP = .06168, 6.2% rounded

5.
$$1,500 \times .12 = \$180.00$$
$$1,500 + 180.00 = \$1,680.00$$
$$1,680.00 \times .12 = \$201.60$$
$$1,680.00 + 201.60 = \$1,881.60$$

6. 12% ÷ 4 = 3% per quarter

Quarter	Principal	Interest (3%)	New Balance
1	1,500.00	45.00	1,545.00
2	1,545.00	46.35	1,591.35
3	1,591.35	47.74	1,639.09
4	1,639.09	49.17	1,688.26
5	1,688.26	50.65	1,738.91
6	1,738.91	52.17	1,791.08
7	1,791.08	53.73	1,844.81
8	1,844.81	55.34	1,900.15

7. 12% ÷ 12 = 1% per month

Month	Principal	Interest	Balance
1	1,500.00	15.00	1,515.00
2	1,515.00	15.15	1,530.15
3	1,530.15	15.30	1,545.45
4	1,545.45	15.45	1,560.90
5	1,560.90	15.61	1,576.51
6	1,576.51	15.77	1,592.28
7	1,592.28	15.92	1,608.20
8	1,608.20	16.08	1,624.28
9	1,624.28	16.24	1,640.52
10	1,640.52	16.41	1,656.93
11	1,656.93	16.57	1,673.50
12	1,673.50	16.74	1,690.24

8. 1,690.24 − 1,500 = 190.24 return

WP x 1,500 = 190.24

$$WP = \frac{190.24}{1,500} \approx .12682 \approx 12.68\%$$

Lesson Practice 6.2

1. 800.00 x .15 = $120.00

2. 15% ÷ 4 = 3.75% per quarter

Quarter	Principal	Interest (.0375)	New Balance
1	800.00	30.00	830.00
2	830.00	31.13	861.13
3	861.13	32.29	893.42
4	893.42	33.50	926.92

3. 15% ÷ 12 = 1.25% per month

Month	Principal	Interest (.0125)	New Balance
1	800.00	10.00	810.00
2	810.00	10.13	820.13
3	820.13	10.25	830.38
4	830.38	10.38	840.76
5	840.76	10.51	851.27
6	851.27	10.64	861.91
7	861.91	10.77	872.68
8	872.68	10.91	883.59
9	883.59	11.04	894.63
10	894.63	11.18	905.81
11	905.81	11.32	917.13
12	917.13	11.46	928.59

4. 928.59 − 800 = 128.59

WP × 800 = 128.59

$WP = \dfrac{128.59}{800} = .1607 = 16.1\%$

5.

Year	Principal	Interest	Balance
1	2,500.00	225.00	2,725.00
2	2,725.00	245.25	2,970.25
3	2,970.25	267.32	3,237.57
4	3,237.57	291.38	3,528.95
5	3,528.95	317.61	3,846.56
6	3,846.56	346.19	4,192.75
7	4,192.75	377.35	4,570.10
8	4,570.10	411.31	4,981.41
9	4,981.41	448.33	5,429.74
10	5,429.74	488.68	5,918.42

6. $6,087.97 You can generate a table for this at mathusee.com/investment_calculator.php

7. $6,128.39 (using Math-U-see Investment Calculator)

8.
```
  6128.36    FV
- 2500.00    deposit
  3628.36    profit
```

WP × 2500 = 3628.36

$WP = \dfrac{3628.36}{2500}$

WP ≈ 1.4513 ≈ 145.13%

145.13 ÷ 10 yrs ≈ 14.5% Annual rate needed to earn same profit on simple interest

Lesson Review 6.3

1. 10,000.00 x .04 = 400.00
400.00 x 3 = 1,200.00

2.

Quarter	Principal	Interest	New Balance
1	10,000.00	100.00	10,100.00
2	10,100.00	101.00	10,201.00
3	10,201.00	102.01	10,303.01
4	10,303.01	103.03	10,406.04
5	10,406.04	104.06	10,510.10
6	10,510.10	105.10	10,615.20
7	10,615.20	106.15	10,721.35
8	10,721.35	107.21	10,828.56
9	10,828.56	108.29	10,936.85
10	10,936.85	109.37	11,046.22
11	11,046.22	110.46	11,156.68
12	11,156.68	111.57	11,268.25

3. $11,272.72

4. This also may be set up like #8 in 6.2.

$\begin{array}{r} 10,000 + WP\,(10,000) \times 3 = 11,272.74 \\ -10,000 \qquad\qquad\qquad -10,000 \end{array}$

WP (10,000) × 3 = 1,272.74

$\dfrac{WP}{\cancel{100}}\,(\overset{100}{\cancel{10,000}}) \times 3 = 1,272.74$

WP × 300 = 1,272.74

$WP = \dfrac{1,272.74}{300}$

WP = 4.24%

5. Electric Bill

6. August 6, 2007

7. 8 x 20% = 1.6 so 8 + 1.60 ≈ $9.60

$$5\% \times 7.95 = .40$$
$$16\% \times 7.95 = 1.27$$
$$.40 + 1.27 = 1.67$$
$$1.67 + 7.95 = \$9.62, \text{ yes}$$

8. forgetting God - *Deuteronomy 8*

9. can provide for family, give to those in need, support and extend God's Kingdom

10. above, coming down from the Father of lights. *James 1:17*

Lesson Review 6.4

1. 2,500.00 x .08 = $200.00

200 x 3 = $600

2.

Quarterly	Principal	Interest	New Balance
1	2,500.00	50.00	2,550.00
2	2,550.00	51.00	2,601.00
3	2,601.00	52.02	2,653.02
4	2,653.02	53.06	2,706.08
5	2,706.08	54.12	2,760.20
6	2,760.20	55.20	2,815.40
7	2,815.40	56.31	2,871.71
8	2,871.71	57.43	2,929.14
9	2,929.14	58.58	2,987.72
10	2,987.72	59.75	3,047.47
11	3,047.47	60.95	3,108.42
12	3,108.42	62.17	3,170.59

3. $3,175.59

4.
$$2,500 + WP(2500) \times 3 = 3,175.59$$
$$-2,500 \qquad\qquad -2,500$$
$$\frac{WP}{100}(2,500) \times 3 = 6.75.59$$
$$WP \times 75 = 675.59$$
$$WP = 9.01\%$$

5. Harry Hundreds, 400 Decimal St., Place Value, PA 01234

6. Place Value Power & Light, $247.89

7. 11 x 2 x .20 = 4.40
4.40 + 22.00 = 26.40
10.95 x .06 = .66
10.95 x .16 = 1.75

$$\begin{array}{r} 10.95 \\ .66 \\ + \ 1.75 \\ \hline 13.36 \times 2 = \$26.72 \end{array}$$

$26.72 is close to estimate of $26.40

8. yes, Hebrews 11:37-40

9. Answers may vary. - Deuteronomy 8:18

10. Let your conversation be without covetousness; and be content with such things as ye have: for he hath said, I will never leave thee, nor forsake thee. **Hebrews 13:5, KJV**

Lesson Practice 7.1

1. 242.73 - 100.00 = $142.73, $242.73 from the investment calculator

2. 242.73 ÷ 2 ≈ 121 gallons

3. 100.00 ÷ .50 = 200 gallons

4. faster

5. **100.00 @ 5%** for 2 years = $110.25

$$FV = 100\left(1+\frac{5\%}{1}\right)^{2\cdot 1}$$

$$FV = 100\left(1.05\right)^{2}$$

$$FV = 110.25$$

100.00 @ 4.5% for 2 years = $109.40

$$FV = 100\left(1+\frac{4.5\%}{12}\right)^{2\cdot 12}$$

$$FV = 100\left(1.00375\right)^{24}$$

$$FV = 109.40$$

The first option yields a larger return

6. $250.00 @ 4% for 3 years = $281.82
$31.82 interest

7. 30 years x 12 months x 100.00
$36,000.00 will grow to $83,225.86

8. 15 years x 12 months x 240.00
$43,200.00 will grow to $64,149.35

(#7 and 8 according to MUS investment calculator. Other methods may yield slightly different results due to differences in rounding.)

9. #7, begin investing while you are young

10. Approximately $1,560.00 using the rule of 72

5. 1,000.00 @ 4.5% for 3 years = 1,141.17

$$FV = 1,000\left(1+\frac{4.5\%}{1}\right)^{3\cdot 1}$$

$$FV = 1,000\left(1.045\right)^{3}$$

$$FV = \$1,141.17$$

1,000.00 @ 3.75%
for 3 years = 1,117.87

$$FV = 1,000\left(1+\frac{3.75\%}{12}\right)^{3\cdot 12}$$

$$FV = 1,000\left(1.003125\right)^{36}$$

$$FV = \$1,118.88$$

The first option yields a larger return

6. 3,000.00 @ 3.5%
for 4 years = 3,450.12.
$450.12 interest

7. 40 years x 12 months x 100.00
$48,000.00 will grow to $152,602.02

8. 25 years x 12 months x 200.00
$60,000.00 will grow to $119,101.94

9. #7

10. Approximately $2,930.00 using the rule of 72

Lesson Practice 7.2

1. Certificate of Deposit
This is a simple investment where you buy a CD and receive interest

2. Individual Retirement Account
This is a vehicle for an individual to set aside funds for retirement.

3. can pay taxes up front and not later

4. greater

Lesson Review 7.3

1. $1,116.94

2. $1,120.42, $ 3.48 difference

3. 200 x 12 x 30 = $72,000

4. $182,722.38

Figure 7

5.

$$FV = P\left(1+\frac{R}{N}\right)^{Y \cdot N}$$

$$FV = 200\left(1+\frac{.0525}{4}\right)^{5 \cdot 4}$$

$$FV = 200\left(1+.013125\right)^{20}$$

$$FV = 200\left(1.013125\right)^{20}$$

$$FV = 259.59$$

6. Answers may vary.

7. See figure 7 above. Date may vary.

8. God

9. by not returning tithes/offerings. Malachi 3:8

10. Malachi 3:10

Lesson Review 7.4

1. $3,011.29

2. $3,024.38
   3,024.38 – 3,011.29 = 13.09
   Difference of $13.09

3. 400 x 12 x 15 = 72,000

4. $109,176.95; same investment but very different results

5.
$$\begin{aligned}182{,}722.38 \\ -\ 109{,}176.95 \\ \hline 73{,}545.43\end{aligned}$$

$$FV = P\left(1+\frac{R}{N}\right)^{Y \cdot N}$$

$$FV = 400\left(1+\frac{.06}{4}\right)^{8 \cdot 4}$$

$$FV = 400\left(1+.015\right)^{32}$$

$$FV = 400\left(1.015\right)^{32} = \$644.13$$

6. Answers may vary.

7.

ENDORSE HERE
_____
Pay to Elma Hundreds
_____
Harry Hundreds
_____
DO NOT WRITE, SIGN, OR STAMP BELOW THIS LINE
Reserved for Financial Institution use

8. our needs

STEWARDSHIP

9. substance - Proverbs 3:9

10. offerings - Malachi 3:8

Lesson Practice 8.1

1. the money that is coming in; salary, self-employment, commissions, etc.

2. Wants are things that you can get along without. Some needs are food, clothing, shelter, and transportation.

3. savings, emergencies, and giving

4. Answers may vary; saving money in an envelope for a specific need

5. Hourly wage is $12.50.

Gross Income.........25,000
1. Tithe 2,500
2. Taxes 4,375
Net Spendable ..18,125.00
3. Housing ....6,887.50 — little high
4. Food ....2,175.00 — 2,286
5. Auto..........2,718.75 — 2,643
6. Insurance .....906.25 — 880
7. Debts ....906.25 — high 900
8. Recreation....906.25 — high 900
9. Clothing ......906.25 — 895
10. Savings........906.25 — 850
11. Medical
    & Dental ......906.25 — low
12. Misc. ....906.25 — 917

Lesson Practice 8.2

1. the money that is being spent; Answers may vary.

2. helps to project needs; reveals spending habits

3. to enable you to be a faithful steward to prepare for savings, emergencies, and giving

4. no; each family has different needs, priorities, personalities, and income

5. Hourly wage is $20.00

Gross Income.........40,000 | 40,000
1. Tithe ....4,000 | 4,000
2. Taxes ....7,200 | 7,200
Net Spendable ....28,800 | 28,800
3. Housing ....8,640 | 8,640
4. Food ....3,456 | 3,380
5. Auto...............3,456 | little high
6. Insurance ....1,440 | 1,437
7. Debts ....1,440 | little low
8. Recreation......2,016 | 2,009
9. Clothing ....1,440 | high
10. Savings...........1,440 | 1,440
11. Medical
    & Dental........1,152 | 1,044
12. Misc. ....2,016 | 1,241
13. Investments....2,304 | 2,250

Lesson Review 8.3

1. Answers may vary.

2. shows your actual out-go!

3. $7.50 (15,000 ÷ 2,000)

Gross Income 15,000
1. Tithe 1,500
2. Taxes 1,200
Net Spendable 12,300
3. Housing....................4,305
4. Food.........................1,845
5. Auto 1,845
6. Insurance 615
7. Debts 615
8. Recreation 615
9. Clothing 615
10. Savings........................615
11. Medical/Dental 615
12. Misc. 615

LESSON PRACTICE 8.1 – LESSON REVIEW 8.3 **185**

4. Clothing & Debts are up and savings is down. Not a good trend if it continues.

```
Gross Income .................15,000
  1.  Tithe ......................1,500
  2.  Taxes .....................1,200
Net Spendable
  3.  Housing...................4,305
  4.  Food.......................1,850
  5.  Auto .......................2,000
  6.  Insurance ..................600
  7.  Debts ..................... ↑845
  8.  Recreation ..................550
  9.  Clothing ............... ↑1,115
 10.  Savings.................... 200↓
 11.  Medical/Dental ...........425
 12.  Misc. ..........................395
```

5.
$$FV = P\left(1+\frac{R}{N}\right)^{Y \cdot N}$$
$$FV = 750\left(1+\frac{.055}{4}\right)^{10 \cdot 4}$$
$$FV = 750(1.01375)^{40}$$
$$FV = 750(1.72677)$$
$$FV = 1295.08$$

6. $Y \times \dfrac{4}{4} = \dfrac{72}{4} = 18$ years

7. The frequency of interest accumulating is what makes compounding so profitable. Simple interest is annual and compounding is multiple.

8. Tending the garden in Eden

9. No, absolutely not. "Whether therefore ye eat, or drink, or whatsoever ye do, do all to the glory of God." *1 Corinthians 10:31 ASV*

10. God's glory, *1 Corinthians 10:31*

Lesson Review 8.4

1. Answers may vary.

2. Answers may vary.

3. $25.00 (50,000 ÷ 2,000)
```
Gross Income .................50,000
  1.  Tithe ......................5,000
  2.  Taxes .....................9,000
Net Spendable ...............36,000
  3.  Housing..................10,800
  4.  Food.......................4,320
  5.  Auto .......................4,320
  6.  Insurance ...............1,800
  7.  Debts .....................1,800
  8.  Recreation ...............2,520
  9.  Clothing .................1,800
 10.  Savings....................1,800
 11.  Medical/Dental .........1,440
 12.  Misc. ......................2,520
 13.  Investment ..............2,880
```

4. Auto is up, recreation is up, savings are up. It's a good thing savings are up because you may need a better car. 11-13 are down but close.

```
Gross Income .........50,000
  1.  Tithe ...........5,000
  2.  Taxes ..........9,000
Net Spendable........36,000
  3.  Housing......11,000
  4.  Food.............4,150
  5.  Auto............4,975 ↑
  6.  Insurance .....1,750
  7.  Debts ..........1,900
  8.  Recreation ...2,700 ↑
  9.  Clothing ......2,400 ↑
 10.  Savings........2,100 ↑
 11.  Medical
        & Dental .... 1,275 ↓
 12.  Misc. ..........2,300 ↓ but close
 13.  Investment ..2,550 ↓ but close
```

5. 8 yrs x 9 % = 72, so we can expect the 6,500 to double to 13,000

6. weekly, the more frequent money is compounded the better your return.

STEWARDSHIP

7.

$$1{,}000\left(1+\frac{.04}{1}\right)^{3\cdot 1} \text{ or}$$

$$1{,}000\left(1+\frac{.0375}{12}\right)^{3\cdot 12}$$

1,000 is not a factor since it is the same for both equations
1.124864 > 1.118876

(If you do it on the Math-U-see investment calculator -
1,124.86 > 1,118.88)

8. sweat and toil

9. A dichotomy treats two things as mutually exclusive. It makes an unbiblical distinction between sacred and secular.

10. All occupations are sacred as we live for Jesus.

Lesson Practice 9.1

1. retail is the cost to the supplier plus his profit; the final customer

2. brings products from many different places to a convenient location for you to purchase

3. rent, salaries, utilities, advertising

4. 40%

5. 4-5%

6. $24.00

7. WP of 59 is 24?
WP = 24/59 ≈ 41% of retail
WP of 35 is 24?
WP = 24/35 ≈ 69% of wholesale

8. 14.99 x .65 ≈ $9.74

9. 40% of Retail is $5.00
.4 x R = 5
R = $12.50

10.
```
  .79       120     1.89      .56
- .55      x .24  - 1.33    x 40
  .24     28.80      .56    22.40
```
Water wins!

Lesson Practice 9.2

1. the price the retailer pays for an item

2. provides products in quantity at good prices; brings products from distant locations

3. transportation, warehouse rental, salaries, possibly travel

4. $\frac{9.00}{16.00} \approx 56\%$

5. $\frac{7.00}{9.00} \approx 78\%$

Rounded to the nearest percent

6. 2.89 – (12% x 2.89) ≈ $2.54
or 100% – 12% = 88%,
so 88% x 2.89 ≈ $2.54

7. 2.89 – 2.54 = $ .35,
2,400 x .35 = $840.00

8. 3,500 ÷ 28 = $125.00

WP of 595 is 125?
WP x 595 = 125,
WP = 125/595 ≈ 21%

9. retail: friends and neighbors; wholesale: Mr. Evans; middleman, Boy Scouts

10. Mr Evans' profit =
$4.00 – $2.50 = $1.50
WP x $2.50 = $1.50
WP = $1.50/$2.50 = .6 = 60%

Boy Scouts' profit =
$7.00 – $4.00 = $3.00
WP x $4.00 = $3.00
WP = $3.00/$4.00 = .75 = 75%
Boy Scouts' percentage was higher

SOLUTIONS

Lesson Review 9.3

1. profit 85¢ – 25¢ = 60¢

$$WP \times \frac{85}{85} = \frac{60}{85}$$

$$WP \times \frac{60}{85} \approx 71\%$$

2. $WP \times .89 = \$ .20$

$$WP \times \frac{89}{89} = \frac{20}{89} \oplus 22\%$$

3. They will push the lemonade since it brings a greater profit

4. Again, the lemonade since they have more room to offer a discount and still make a profit.

5. Answers may vary.

6. Answers may vary.

7.

$$FV = P\left(1 + \frac{R}{N}\right)^{Y \cdot N}$$

$$2{,}000\left(1 + \frac{.07}{1}\right)^{5 \cdot 1} \text{or } 2{,}000\left(1 + \frac{.07}{12}\right)^{5 \cdot 12}$$

$(1.07)^5$	$(1.00583)^{60}$
1.40255	1.41734
× 2000	× 2,000
2,805.10	2,834.68

The second option yields a greater return.

8. yes, Luke 10:7 - And in the same house remain, eating and drinking such things as they give: for the labourer is worthy of his hire.

9. No. The pastor and his wife will not have the benefit of owning their own home for their retirement income.

10. Deuteronomy 25:4

Lesson Review 9.4

1. 1,700 ÷ 500 = $3.40

2. A   7.50 – 3.40 = $4.10
   B   14.99 – 7.50 = $7.49

3. 1,700 ÷ 7.50 ≈ 226.67, so 227 books

4. 14.99 – 3.40 = 11.59
   1,700 ÷ 11.59 ≈ 146.68
   so 147 books
   WP × 14.99 = 11.59

   $$WP \times \frac{14.99}{14.99} = \frac{11.59}{14.99}$$

   WP ≈ 77%

5. Answers may vary.

6. Answers may vary.

7.

$$FV = 500\left(1 + \frac{.08}{1}\right)^{4 \cdot 1}$$

$$FV = 500(1.08)^4 \approx \$680.24$$

8. In their personal estate, which is usually their home

9. Answers may vary, but I lean towards 1 Corinthians 9:14 -

   Even so did the Lord ordain that they that proclaim the gospel should live of the gospel. *ASV*

10. Help everybody, but especially your brothers and sisters in Christ.

Lesson Practice 10.1

1. don't have to carry cash; money for emergencies; rebates or special offers

2. tend to spend more; high interest rates, fees

3. choose one with useful perks; compare all fees; pay off balance each month

4. The finance charge is the amount the company charges, based on a percent of the unpaid balance; There is a late charge if the minimum payment is not made in time.

5. annual percentage rate, divide by 12 for monthly interest rate

6. $15\% \div 12 = 1.25\%$

7. $1\ 1/8\% \times 12 = 13.5\%$

8.

Payment	Monthly Payment	Interest	Principle Paid	Balance
		(1.25%)		600.00
1	29.09	7.50	21.59	578.41
2	29.09	7.23	21.86	556.55
3	29.09	6.96	22.13	534.42
		$21.69	$65.58	

9. 3 payments, $65.58

10. 3 payments, $21.69

Lesson Practice 10.2

1. credit card borrows money; debit card takes money out of your account

2. you cannot spend beyond your means

3. fees and overdrafts

4. read the fine print; talk to your bank; keep track of purchases

5. The grace period is the length of time you have to make payments without paying interest or late fees. If the balance is not paid each month, the grace period disappears.

6. $21\% \div 12 = 1.75\%$

7. $2\ 1/4\% \times 12 = 27\%$

8.

Payment	Monthly Payment	Interest	Principle Paid	Balance
		(2.00%)		750.00
1	29.42	15.00	14.42	735.58
2	29.42	14.71	14.71	720.87
3	29.42	14.42	15.00	705.87
		44.13	44.13	

9. 3 payments, $44.13

10. 3 payments, $44.13

Lesson Review 10.3

1. $1.125 \times 12 = 13.5\%$

2.

Payment	Monthly Payment	Interest	Principle Paid	Balance
		(21%)		800.00
1	74.49	14.00	60.49	739.51
2	74.49	12.94	61.55	677.96
3	74.49	11.86	62.63	615.33

3. 60.49
   61.55
   + 62.63
   $184.67

4. 14.00
   12.94
   + 11.86
   $38.80

5. $2.50 \times 4 - 10.00$
   $10.00 - 8.50 = \$1.50$

6. $2.50 - 1.40 = 1.10$ per box
   $1.10 \times 4 = 4.40$

7. $2,803.91

SOLUTIONS

8. Yes, God created man to work. Work is a practical way to love your neighbors. Work develops godly character qualities such as diligence.

9. in the garden of Eden

10. Work done well encourages healthy self-esteem and sense of satisfaction as I serve others. Work fosters an environment where you can exhibit integrity and honesty.

Lesson Review 10.4

1. $15 \div 12 = 1\frac{3}{12} = 1\frac{1}{4}$

2.

Payment	Monthly Payment	Interest (18%)	Principle Paid	Balance
				1,250.00
1	36.72	18.75	17.97	1,232.03
2	36.72	18.48	18.24	1,213.79
3	36.72	18.21	18.51	1,195.28

3. 17.97
   18.24
   + 18.51
   54.72

4. 18.75
   18.48
   + 18.21
   55.44

5. 75 − 52 = 23
   WP x 75 = 23
   $WP \times \frac{75}{75} = \frac{23}{75}$
   WP = 31%

6. 100% x 1.75 = 1.75
   1.75 + 1.75 = 3.50

7. Answers may vary.

8. 6; 6 x 52 = 312
   Ten Commandments, Exodus 20:9-10

9. As you work, you serve others as you would like to be served yourself.

10. Deuteronomy 5:13

Exodus is the 2nd book
10 commandments
2 x 10 = 20, so found in Exodus 20

Deuteronomy is the 5th book in the Bible, so Deuteronomy 5

Lesson Practice 11.1

1. The Buying club

Buying Club
100 oz cheerios ......6.25 x 2 = 12.50
30 lb apples ....5.99 x 3 = 17.97
mileage ....40 x .25 = 10.00
12.50 + 17.97 + 10.00 = $40.47

Fergie's grocery
100 oz cheerios ......4.19 x 5 = 20.95
30 lb apples ....2.49 x 10 = 24.90
mileage ....16 x .25 = 4.00
20.95 + 24.90 + 4.00 = $49.85

2. The Buying club

Buying Club
256 oz juice ....8.29 x 1 = 8.29
36 2-pk cups ....13.39 x 1 = 13.39
mileage ....40 x .25 = 10.00
8.29 + 13.39 + 10 = 31.68

Fergie's grocery
256 oz juice ....2.99 x 4 = 11.96
36 2-pk cups ....59 x 36 = 21.24
mileage ....16 x .25 = 4.00
11.96 + 21.24 + 4.00 = 37.20

3. 12 large eggs at 2.88¢ per oz
$1.09 18 lg 36 oz = 3.03¢ per oz
$ .69 12 lg 24 oz = 2.88¢ per oz
$ .39 6 lg 12 oz = 3.25¢ per oz

4. Costco with 3.9¢ per in²

Papa Johns – $13.55, 14" dia. =
$(3.14)(7^2)$ = 153.86 in² = 8.8¢ per in²

Pizza Hut – $14.24, 14" dia. =
$(3.14)(7^2)$ = 153.86 in² = 9.3¢ per in²

Dominos – $13.49, 14" dia. =
$(3.14)(7^2)$ = 153.86 in² = 8.8¢ per in²

Cousins Pizza – $10.75, 16" dia. =
$(3.14)(8^2)$ = 200.96 in² = 5.3¢ per in²

Costco – $9.95, 18" dia. =
$(3.14)(9^2)$ = 254.34 in² = 3.9¢ per in²

5. taste, quality of ingredients, proximity, price of soft drinks

Lesson Practice 11.2

1. Good's Store – $34.93

Home Depot
$1.44 ÷ 1,500 = .96/hr
light bulbs .... .96 x 5 = 4.80
100# seed ....8.88 x 4 = 35.52
mileage ....40 x .25 = 10.00

Total $50.32

Good's Store
light bulbs............... .99 x 5 = 4.95
100# seed............12.99 x 2 = 25.98
mileage.................16 x .25 = 4.00

Total $34.93

Buck Hardware
light bulbs..............1.39 x 5 = 6.95
100# seed............5.99 x 10 = 59.90
mileage ....9 x .25 = 2.25

Total $69.10

2. Good's Store – $69.97

Home Depot
fertilizer ....22.98 x 3 = 68.94
mileage ....40 x .25 = 10.00

Total $78.94

Good's Store
fertilizer ....21.99 x 3 = 65.97
mileage ....16 x .25 = 4.00

Total $69.97

Buck Hardware
fertilizer ....36.98 x 3 = 110.94
mileage ....9 x .25 = 2.25
Total $113.19

3. Grocery – $7.63

Convenience
Sprite - 2 liters...........1.89 x 1 = 1.89
12 cans Sprite .... .75 x 12 = 9.00
mileage ....2 x .25 = .50

Total $11.39

Grocery
Sprite - 2 liters...........1.39 x 1 = 1.39
12 cans Sprite ....3.99 = 3.99
mileage ....9 x .25 = 2.25

Total $7.63

4. Convenience Store - $7.75

Convenience
milk - 1 gal................3.06 x 1 = 3.06
ice cream ....4.19 x 1 = 4.19
mileage ....2 x .25 = .50

Total $7.75

Grocery
milk - 1 gal................3.22 x 1 = 3.22
ice cream ....4.79 x 1 = 4.79
mileage ....9 x .25 = 2.25

Total $10.26

5. some items cheaper, proximity as opposed to a grocery store for variety

6. medium is the best buy

$ .79 12 jumbo 30 oz = 2.63¢ per oz
$ .79 12 x-lg 27 oz = 2.93¢ per oz
$ .69 12   lg   24 oz = 2.88¢ per oz
$ .49 12 med. 21 oz = 2.33¢ per oz

Lesson Review 11.3

1. 16 oz = 1 pint
   4 qt in 1 gallon

2. 1 gallon is 128 ounces,
   $4.04 \div 128 = .032$ or 3.2¢

   1/2 gallon is 64 ounces
   $2.07 \div 64 = .032$ or 3.2¢

   1 quart is 32 ounces
   $1.09 \div 32 = .034$ or 3.4¢

   1 pint is 16 ounces
   $.79 \div 16 = .049$ or 4.9¢

3. There is very little difference in price between a gallon, a half gallon, and a quart. So buy what you will use before the expiration date.

4. Answers may vary.

5. Profit
   14.99 – 3.40 = $11.59 per book
   80 x 11.59 = $927.20
   927.20 – 225 (ad) = **$702.20**
   I think so.

6. 175 x 11.59 = $2,028.25
   2,028.25 – 25.00 = 2,003.25

7. $18 \div 12 = 1\frac{6}{12} = 1\frac{1}{2}\%$

8. the church; I Timothy 5:3 & 16

9. one who doesn't provide for his own, especially his own household
   I Timothy 5:8

10. a woman, a **worthy** one!

Lesson Review 11.4

1. **Grocery Store**
   20 rolls – $.70 per roll
   4 rolls – $.75 per roll
   1 roll – $.69 per roll

   Buying Club
   30 rolls - $.59 per roll

2. Buying Club

3. The second best buy is a single roll for 69¢. Yes, this is a surprise because usually when you buy larger quantities there is a discount.

4. Grocery store
   the difference is $4.50

   5 x .30 = 1.50
   20 x .30 = 6.00

   6 - 1.50 = $4.50

5. 120 x .25 = $30.00 in savings

6. 120 x .30 = 36.00
   120 – 36 = 84.00
   84.00 x .25 = 21.00
   84 – 21 = $63.00

7.
$$2\frac{1}{8} \times 12 =$$
$$24 + \frac{12}{8} =$$
$$24 + 1\frac{1}{2} = 25\frac{1}{2}\%$$

8. Amen.

9. practical

10. Jesus in the Lord's Prayer in Matthew 6:11 and Luke 11:3

Lesson Practice 12.1

1. **Plan A**

	100	250	500	1,000
4.5¢ per min	4.50	11.25	22.50	45.00
2.50 per mo.	2.50	2.50	2.50	2.50
Price per min	7¢	5.5¢	5¢	4.75¢

Plan B

5.5¢ per min	5.50	13.75	27.50	55.00
0 per month				
Price per min	5.5¢	5.5¢	5.5¢	5.5¢

2. Plan A

3. 7.14 per day; 214 minutes

per month; plan B

4. $.045M + 2.50 = .055M$

Mult. by 1,000

$45M + 2,500 = 55M$

Subtract 45M

$2,500 = 10M$

Divide by 10

$M = 250$

5. **Plan A**

	100	250	500	1,000
2.5¢ per min	2.50	6.25	12.50	25.00
3.00 per mo.	3.00	3.00	3.00	3.00
Price per min	5.5¢	3.7¢	3.1¢	2.8¢

Plan B

4¢ per min	4.00	10.00	20.00	40.00
0 per month				
Price per min	4¢	4¢	4¢	4¢

6. Plan A

7. Plan B

$5 \times 30 = 150,$
$150 \times .025 + 3.00 = 6.75,$
$150 \times .04 = \$6.00$

8. $.025M + 3.00 = .04M$

Multiply by 1,000

$25M + 3,000 = 40M$

Subtract 25M

$3,000 = 15M$

Divide by 15

$M = 200$

Lesson Practice 12.2

1. **Plan A - 250 anytime minutes**

	100	250	500	1,000
$40 a mo.	40	40	40	40
45¢ add'l min.			112.50	337.50
Price per min	40¢	16¢	30.5¢	37.75¢

Plan B - 500 anytime minutes

$60 per mo.	60.00	60.00	60.00	60.00
35¢ add'l min.				175.00
Price per min	60¢	24¢	12¢	23.5¢

Plan C - 1000 anytime minutes

$100 per mo.	100	100	100	100
25¢ add'l min				
Price per min	$1.00	40¢	20¢	10¢

2. Plan A = $40 + (50 \times .45) = \$62.50$

Plan B = $60

Plan C = $100.00

3. **Plan A = $40**

Plan B = $60

Plan C = $100.00

4. Plan A = $40 + (650 \times .45) = \$332.50$

Plan B = $60 + (40 \times .35) = \$200.00$

Plan C = $100.00

5. which plan you choose will be determined by how many minutes you need each month

6. coverage area, friends with the same plan, charge for the phone itself

Lesson Review 12.3

1. Answers may vary.

2. Answers may vary.

3. the Buying Club

given 2 in a pack, 6 packs to make 12

Grocery Store
$4.99 x 6 = 29.94 for 12 batteries
5 x .30 = $1.50
29.94 + 1.50 = $31.44

Buying Club
$10.49 for 12 batteries
20 x .30 = 6.00
10.49 + 6.00 = $16.49

4. the Buying Club

Grocery Store
Since 8 in a pack, you will need
72 ÷ 8 or 9 packs.
4.99 x 9 = $44.91
5 x .30 = $1.50
44.91 + 1.50 = $46.41

Buying Club
Since 36 in a pack,
72 ÷ 36 = 2 packs.
12.89 x 2 = 25.78
20 x .30 = 6.00
25.78 + 6.00 = 31.78

5. 25D ÷ 5D = 5
5 x .10 = $.50 off each gallon
2.59 − .50 = 2.09
20 gallons x 2.09 = 41.80
compared to 20 x 2.59 = 51.80
She spent $250 to save $10.

$$\frac{10}{250} = 4\%$$

6. 170 ÷ 50 = 3.4 so 3 x .10 = 30¢
32 x 30¢ = $9.60 saved

7. $20 \div 12 = 1\frac{8}{12} = 1\frac{2}{3}\%$

8. For I am the LORD, I change not;
therefore ye sons of Jacob are not
consumed. *Malachi 3:6*

Jesus Christ the same yesterday, and
to day, and for ever. *Hebrews 13:8*

9. No. Paul did in Romans, Galatians,
and 2 Corinthians

10. Hudson Taylor & George Müller

Lesson Review 12.4

1. Answers may vary.

2. Answers may vary.

3. the Buying Club - $17.89

Grocery Store
100 x .25 = $25.00
5 x .30 = $1.50
25.00 + 1.50 = $26.50

Buying Club
100 for $11.89
20 x .30 = $6.00
11.89 + 6.00 = $17.89

4. Grocery Store - $23.02

Grocery Store
48 ÷ 6 = 8
8 x 2.69 = $21.52
5 x .30 = $1.50
21.52 + 1.50 = $23.02

Buying Club
48 ÷ 24 = 2
2 x 9.99 = $19.98
20 x .30 = 6.00
19.98 + 6.00 = $25.98

5. WP x 16,000 = 350

$$Wp \times \frac{16,000}{16,000} = \frac{350}{16,000}$$

WP = 2.2%

6. WP x 19,200 = 350

$$Wp \times \frac{19,200}{19,200} = \frac{350}{19,200}$$

WP = 1.8%

7. $2\frac{1}{2} \times 12 = 24 + \frac{12}{2} = 24 + 6 = 30\%$

8. George Müller; Hudson Taylor

9. Galatians 2:10

10. The length of your life,
    what you eat, and your clothes.

    Matthew 6:25-31

Lesson Practice 13.1

1. Value is intangible. It includes customer service and high quality. Price is dollars and cents.

2. information, knowledge, and customer service.

3. higher price & limited inventory.

4. KB is 2^{10}, or 1,024 bytes
   MB is 1 megabyte

5. 2,000 KB < 3 MB
   1,000 x 2,000 < 1,000,000 x 3

6. random access memory, bytes

7. My sons opted for the 2nd PC. Here are their reasons:

   1 - The first one is a good deal, but lacks a good warranty.

   2 - The second has everything they felt they needed, with the only difference being the speed of the processor.

Lesson Practice 13.2

1. A warranty doesn't last for the life of the product, as does a lifetime guarantee. A warranty is the pledge of the company to stand behind their product.

2. the large stock of inventory; lower prices.

3. limited variety within a product line, distance to travel, lack of knowledgeable employees.

4. GB is 2^{30}, or 1,073,741,824 bytes

5. 1 GB = 1024 MB
   .5 GB = 512 MB
   512 MB > 500 MB: .5 GB is greater

6. a unit of frequency, flashes per second in monitors

7. My 3 sons opted for the 2nd Apple.

   Here are their reasons:
   1 - The graphics card was better.

   2 - They didn't feel the extra processing speed and memory warranted the $500.00 difference.

Lesson Review 13.3

1. They are banking on your using the same printer once it is installed and continuing to buy inkjet cartridges from them.

2. This will vary, but generally when it is an item that you value.

3. Answers may vary.

4. Answers may vary.

5. Having a land line makes it possible to access the internet.

6. Answers may vary.

7. When you are comparing prices, make sure you are comparing the same quantities on the same size or the same model, etc. Apples to apples means as much as possible compare the same items.

8. children's children

9. a physical or earthly inheritance; an eternal heavenly inheritance.

10. emergencies, retirement, nest egg

Lesson Review 13.4

1. Answers may vary.

2. Answers may vary.

3. Answers may vary.

4. Answers may vary.

5. Answers may vary.

6. Answers may vary.

7. Sometimes a store will divide the item you are researching into the price per piece or the price per ounce. This is the price per individual unit.

8. Levi

9. the prodigal son (Luke 15)

10. no (Proverbs 20:21)

Lesson Practice 14.1

1. a lessening of value; cars and computers

2. after one year, $15,085
after two years, $12,705

3. $2,988.39

4. $116.66; $2.77; almost all of the principal has been paid

5. $9,270; more; 25,000 is low mileage for a four year old car

6. interest rate, cost of the vehicle, and the down payment.

7. 2-4 years old, good condition

8. better value, still relatively new, much cheaper

9. pray and research

10. Internet sites

Lesson Practice 14.2

1. appreciate, real estate

2. after three years, $9,892
after four years, $11,727

3. $20,000

4. 48

5. insurance requirements, rebate details, length of loan

6. a rental agreement

7. open, closed

8. nope

9. kbb.com, edmunds.com, nadaguides.com

10. ebaymotors.com for used, carsdirect.com for new...

Lesson Review 14.3

1. Answers may vary.

2. Answers may vary.

3. Answers may vary.

4. Answers may vary.

5. Answers may vary.

6. Answers may vary.

7. $2.99 ÷ 3 = $1.00 each piece

$4.99 ÷ 5 = $1.00

$7.99 ÷ 10 = 80¢

The third option is the best per unit price. But are you that hungry? The two that are virtually the same are the first two options.

8. because where your treasure is, there will your heart be also

9. Steve pays for heating oil while Sandi oversees and budgets for household needs.

10. First keep a careful journal of what you actually spend, or your out-go. Then look at your net take-home pay to determine your in-come. With this data you are able to begin establishing your financial priorities and objectives.

Lesson Review 14.4

1. Answers may vary.
2. Answers may vary.
3. Answers may vary.
4. Answers may vary.
5. Answers may vary.
6. Answers may vary.

7. $1\frac{1}{3}\% \times 12 = 12 + \frac{12}{3} = 12 + 4 = 16\%$

8. Crown Ministries at crown.org
9. His beloved bride—Sandi Beth
10. weaker; 1 Peter 3:7

Lesson Practice 15.1

1. 443 mi ÷ 19 gal = 23.3 mi per gal
2. 19 gal x $2.19 per gal = $41.61
3. $41.61 ÷ 443 mi = .0939 = 9.4¢
4. WP x 509 = 260
   WP = 260/509 = 51%
5. depreciation
6. (9,270.00 − 7,340.00) ÷ 15,000 = 13¢
7. 1,600.00 ÷ 15,000 =
   .1066 = 10.7¢ per mi
8. 509.00 ÷ 15,000 =
   .0339 = 3.4¢ per mi
9. $509 − $260 = $249.00
10. 1,982 ÷ (52 x 20) = $1.91 per mi

Lesson Practice 15.2

1. 382 mi ÷ 12.5 gal = 30.6 mi per gal

2. $2.19 per gal x 12.5 gal = $27.38
3. $27.38 ÷ 382 mi = 7¢
4. WP x 578 = 260, WP = 260/578 = 45%
5. gasoline and insurance
6. (20,997 − 15,085) ÷ 15,000 = 39.4¢
7. $1,467 ÷ 15,000 = .0978 = 9.8¢/mi
8. $578 ÷ 15,000 = .0385 = 3.9¢/mi
9. $578 − $260 = $318
10. 1/4 x 7 = 7/4 bales per week
    $20 ÷ 7/4 = 11.4 mi/bale

Lesson Review 15.3

1. 13,219.7 − 12,972.2 = 247.5 mi
2. 247.5 ÷ 11.3 = 21.9 mpg
3. $2.75 x 11.3 = $31.08
4. cost per mile is
   $31.08 ÷ 247.50 = 12.6¢ per mi
5. Answers may vary.
6. You don't have to pay a middleman if you deal directly with the seller. You have a larger geographical area, so a larger selection of cars from which to choose. It is easier to compare cars and research their value. You may shop without leaving your home. There may be others.

7. $\frac{27}{12} = 2\frac{3}{12} = 2\frac{1}{4}\%$

8. presume - to take for granted (synonym - to assume)
9. To presume on the future is to assume that all things will remain the same. We don't know the future and cannot take it for granted.
10. no; yes; Deuteronomy 15:1-2

SOLUTIONS

Lesson Review 15.4

1. 98,104 – 97,555 = 549 mi

2. 30 ÷ $2.80 = 10.7 gal
10.7 + 19 = 29.7 gal

3. 549 ÷ 29.7 = 18.5 mi per gal

4. 19 gallons x $2.80 = $53.20
$53.20 + $30.00 = $83.20
cost per mile –
$83.20 ÷ 549 = 15¢ per mi

5. You can't drive the car or see it. Pictures and descriptions are nice, but they can't replace a test drive. There is a cost to ship the car if you purchase online.

6. any or all of the websites referenced in lesson 14, page 78

7. 500 x .025 = $12.50

8. Psalm 19:13
Keep me from deliberate sins! Don't let them control me. Then I will be free of guilt and innocent of great sin. (Answers may vary, depending on version used.)

9. Appreciation means items will increase in value over time. Depreciation is the opposite of appreciation; items will de-value or lose their value over time.

10. Some items that depreciate are cars, computers, and electronic items, although some cars will become antiques and in a long period of time be worth more. Generally cars wear out.

Lesson Practice 16.1

1. 11/16"

2. 13/16"

3. 14 mm < 15 mm

4. 13/16" < 7/8" (14/16)

5. 180 mm

6. 60% of 180 = .6 x 180 = 108 mm
10 mm = .4 in
10.8 x 10 mm = 10.8 x .4 in
108 mm = 4.32 in
or by using unit multipliers
$108 \text{ mm} \times \frac{.4 \text{ in}}{10 \text{ mm}} = 4.32 \text{ in}$

7. 14"
2.5 x 14" = 35 cm or 350 mm

8. 14" + 4.32" + 4.32" = 22.64"
350 + 108 + 108 = 566 mm

9. (Distance) = (Rate)(Time)
(3,600) = (70)(Time)
3,600 ÷ 70 = Time = 51.4 sec
10 mi is 514.3 sec =
8 min 34.3 sec

10. (Distance) = (Rate)(Time)
(3,600) = (Rate)(62)
3,600 ÷ 62 = Rate = 58.06 mph

11. If you were going 60 mph it would take you 5 minutes to go 5 miles, or 1 mile per minute. So you are going slower.
5:25 = 325 sec ÷ 5 = 65 sec per mi
3,600 ÷ 65 = 55.38 mph

Lesson Practice 16.2

1. 9/16"

2. 11/16"

3. 11 mm > 9 mm

4. 3/8" = 6/16"

5. 175 mm

6. 55% of 175 = 96.25 mm
10 mm = .4 in
96.25 x 10 mm = 96.25 x .4 in
96.25 mm = 3.85 in
or by using unit multipliers

$$96.25 \text{ mm} \times \frac{4 \text{ in}}{10 \text{ mm}} = \mathbf{3}.85 \text{ in}$$

7. 13"; 13 x 25 = 325 mm

8. 13" + 3.85" + 3.85" = 20.7"
   325 + 96.25 + 96.25 = 517.50 mm

9. (Distance) = (Rate)(Time)
   (3,600) = (55)(Time)
   3,600 ÷ 55 = Time = 65.45 sec
   10 mi: 654.5 sec = 10 min 54.5 sec

10. (Distance) = (Rate)(Time)
    (3,600) = (Rate)(57)
    3,600 ÷ 57 = Rate = 63.16 mph

11. If you are going 60 mph it would take you 10 minutes to go 10 mi. So you are going faster.
    8:10 = 490 sec ÷ 10 = 49 sec
    3,600 ÷ 49 = 73.47 mph

Lesson Review 16.3

1. Answers may vary.

2. Answers may vary.

3. Answers may vary.

4. Answers may vary.

5. Answers may vary.

6. Answers may vary.

7. Answers may vary.

8. *Under the Influence*
   by Alvin J. Schmidt

9. No. If you are faithful in little, you will be faithful in much.

10. 40%

Lesson Review 16.4

1. D = RT

   A. $1 \text{ mi} = 30 \frac{\text{miles}}{\text{hour}} \cdot T$

   $\frac{1 \text{ hr}}{30 \text{ mi}} \times 1 \text{ mi} = T$

   $\frac{1 \text{ hr}}{30 \text{ mi}} \times 1 \text{ mi} = \frac{1 \text{ hr}}{30} \times \frac{60 \text{ minutes}}{1 \text{ hr}}$
   $= 2 \text{ min}$

   B. $10 \text{ mi} \times 2 \text{ min} = 20 \text{ minutes}$

   $10 \text{ mi} = 30 \frac{\text{mi}}{\text{hr}} \cdot T$

   $\frac{1 \text{ hr}}{30 \text{ mi}} \times 10 \text{ mi} = \frac{10 \text{ hr}}{30} \times \frac{60 \text{ min}}{1 \text{ hr}}$
   $= 20 \text{ min}$

2. A. $1 \text{ mi} = 45 \frac{\text{mi}}{\text{hr}} \cdot T$

   $\frac{1 \text{ hr}}{45 \text{ mi}} \times \frac{1 \text{ mi}}{1} = T$

   $\frac{1 \text{ hr}}{45} \times \frac{60}{45} \text{ min} = 1\frac{15}{45} = 1\frac{1}{3} \text{ min}$

   or 1 minute 20 seconds

   B. $1\frac{1}{3} \times 10 = 10 + \frac{10}{3} = 13\frac{1}{3} \text{ min}$

   13 minutes 20 seconds

3. D = RT
   $3 \text{ mi} = R \times 9 \text{ min}$
   $3 \text{ mi} = R \times \frac{3}{20} \text{ hr}$
   $20(3 \text{ mi}) = \left(R \times \frac{3}{20} \text{ hr} \right) 20$
   $60 \text{ mi} = 3R \text{ hr}$
   $20 \text{ mi/hr} = R$

4. $D = RT$

   $T = 15$ minutes

   $$\frac{15\ \text{min}}{1} \times \frac{1\ \text{hr}}{60\ \text{min}} = \frac{15}{60}\ \text{hr}$$

   $$\frac{1}{4}\ \text{hr}$$

   $$11\ \text{mi} = R \cdot \frac{1}{4}\ \text{hr}$$

   $$\frac{4}{1\ \text{hr}} \times 11\ \text{mi} = R$$

   $$44\ \frac{\text{mi}}{\text{hr}} = R$$

5. $21{,}000 - 12{,}500 = \$8{,}500$ in 3 yrs

6. $8{,}500 \div 3 = \$2{,}833.33$ per year

7. $12{,}500 - 9{,}500 = \$3{,}000$ for 2 years
   $3{,}000 \div 2 = \$1{,}500$ per year

8. You will establish giving as a habit and a normal part of the Christian life.

9. Answers may vary.

10. So ministries will have funds on which to operate throughout the year. You can incorporate giving into your regular budget. You won't be susceptible to "sales pitches" that prey on your emotions to give.

Lesson Practice 17.1

1. customer service, track record and financial solvency

2. a contract between you and an agency

3. the fee you pay for the service the agency is providing

4. $330.00 (55% of $600)

5. collision and comprehensive

6. probably not, it is not worth repairing

7. I think so, because for a few hundred dollars you are able to protect your investment of several thousand.

8. This is the amount you pay before your insurance policy begins to kick in and pay.

9. The first number is the limit of the liability for one person (in thousands), and the second number is the liability for the accident (in thousands).

Lesson Practice 17.2

1. Your premium will be less because your deductible is higher and the agency will have to pay less.

2. Statistics show that the risk, or chance that they will get in an accident, is much higher for teens.

3. It should be high, because you rarely have a claim on your home.

4. Members sharing each other's expenses.

5. Samaritan Ministries and Christian Care Ministry

6. Permanent is like owning a house (or a policy) while Term is like renting a home or a policy.

7. Insurance Information Institute, www.iii.org

8. The Underinsured Motorist does not have enough coverage, and if the bills are beyond his limits, your insurance will have to make up the difference.

9. In the culture in which we live, it seems the better part of wisdom to at least have protection for very high expenses that could cost you all you have worked and saved for. I think it is part of being a prudent steward.

Lesson Review 17.3

1. Answers may vary.

STEWARDSHIP

2. Answers may vary.

3. Answers may vary.

4. Answers may vary.

5. $\dfrac{1}{2} = \dfrac{8}{16}, \dfrac{9}{16}, \dfrac{3}{8} = \dfrac{6}{16}, \dfrac{7}{16}$

$\dfrac{6}{16}, \dfrac{7}{16}, \dfrac{8}{16}, \dfrac{9}{16}$ or $\dfrac{3}{8}, \dfrac{7}{16}, \dfrac{1}{2}, \dfrac{9}{16}$

6. 14 mm, 13 mm, 12 mm, 11 mm
   Yes, amen.

7. If 1 in = 2.5 cm = 25 mm,
   then 1/2 in = 12.5 mm.

   $\dfrac{5}{8}$ in $= \dfrac{5}{8}$ in $\times \dfrac{2.5 \text{ cm}}{1 \text{ in}} =$

   $\dfrac{12.5 \text{ cm}}{8} = 15\dfrac{5}{8}$ mm

   $\dfrac{125 \text{ mm}}{8} = \begin{array}{r} 15\ \frac{5}{8}\text{mm} \\ 8\overline{)\,125} \\ \underline{8} \\ 45 \\ \underline{40} \\ 5 \end{array}$

   15 mm
   ascending: 10 mm,
   1/2 in (12.5 mm), 15 mm, 5/8 in
   (15 5/8 mm or 15.625 mm)

8. the grace of giving

   2 Corinthians 8:2—their liberality,

   2 Corinthians 8:3—they gave
   of their own accord

9. by asking and believing
   for grace to be given.

10. Philippi

Lesson Review 17.4

1. Split Lmits, Property Damage, PIP,
   Comprehensive, Collision

2. $1,439 - $1,380 = $59

3. $752 - $100 deductible = $652.

4. $625 - $500 deductible = $125 paid
   by insurance

   My premium will most likely increase.

5. $\dfrac{3}{16}, \dfrac{1}{4} = \dfrac{4}{16}, \dfrac{3}{8} = \dfrac{6}{16}, \dfrac{3}{4} = \dfrac{12}{16}$
   largest to smallest

   $\dfrac{3}{4}\left(\dfrac{12}{16}\right), \dfrac{3}{8} \text{ in}\left(\dfrac{6}{16}\right), \dfrac{1}{4} \text{ in}\left(\dfrac{4}{16}\right), \dfrac{3}{16}$

6. descending - 18mm, 15mm,
   13mm, 10mm

7. ascending - 6mm, 1/4" (6.25 mm) 7mm,
   5/16" (7 13/16 mm)

   $\dfrac{1}{4}$ in $\times \dfrac{2.5 \text{ cm}}{1 \text{ in}} = \dfrac{2.5 \text{ cm}}{4} =$

   $\dfrac{25 \text{ mm}}{4} = 6.25$ mm

   $\dfrac{5}{16}$ in $\times \dfrac{2.5 \text{ cm}}{1 \text{ in}} = \dfrac{12.5 \text{ cm}}{16} =$

   $\dfrac{125 \text{ mm}}{16} = 7.81$ mm

8. As you give, or water, others, you shall
   receive and be watered yourself.

9. He can expect God to provide his own
   needs who has graciously given to meet
   the needs of others.

10. 1 John 5:14-15

Lesson Practice 18.1

1. The landlord is responsible, and you have no property taxes to pay.

2. You aren't developing equity because you don't own it.

3. This is an outstanding debt or obligation which is attached to the title and reimbursed to the creditor upon the sale of the property.

4. $3,750.00 ($125,000 x .03)

5. buyer broker represents the buyer; $3,750.00

6. In the event of an unreported lien or an inheritance issue, the insurance covers this obligation.

7. 2 1/4% or .0225

8. 3

9. This decreases the principal, and less principal means less interest on the principal.

Lesson Practice 18.2

1. You are investing in your home and developing a retirement fund in the form of your personal estate.

2. up-front costs such as closing costs, down payment, taxes, and repair costs

3.

	Monthly Pay	Total Principle	Total Interest	# Payment
Standard	584.59	100,000.00	75,377.01	300
Standard plus 50	634.59	100,000.00	63,124.36	258
Standard plus 100	684.59	100,000.00	54,455.71	226
Biweekly	292.30	100,000.00	63,203.19	≈566
Extra Payment	584.59	100,000.00	63,249.93	≈283

4. The third option significantly reduces the interest and number of payments, if you can afford it.

5. Answers may vary.

6. MI is monthly income
30% x MI = 600,
MI = 600/.30 = 2,000
2,000 per month

Lesson Review 18.3

1. Answers may vary.

2. Answers may vary.

3. Using the guidelines for a gross income of $25,000, housing should be 38% of your net spendable income.

   25,000 – 2,500 (tithe) – 4,375 (17.5% taxes) = $18,125
   18,125 x 38% = $6,887.50 per yr
   6,887.50 ÷ 12 = $573.96 per mo.

   Since this is for housing which includes electricity, water, fuel oil, etc., the figure you should be looking at is no more than about $360 for rent or a mortgage payment.

4. $7.50 x 2,000 = $15,000 per yr

   Using the recommendations in the budgeting lesson, 35% is for housing. First find the net spendable. 15,000 – 1,500 (tithe) – 1,200 (8% taxes) = $12,300.
   35% x 12,300 = $4,305 per yr
   4,305 ÷ 12 = $358.75 per mo

   Since this is for housing which includes electricity, water, fuel oil, etc., the figure you should be looking at is $450–$500 for rent or a mortgage payment

5. $475 x 10 = $4,750

6. the value of the policy, or $500,000

7. Answers may vary.

8. your needy neighbor, the widow and fatherless, the poor, Christian workers at home, Christian workers abroad.

9. Answers may vary.

10. You might spend time with him and be a big brother or friend.

Lesson Review 18.4

1. Answers may vary.

2. Answers may vary.

3. Answers may vary.

4. Answers may vary.

5. $360 x 20 = $7,200

6. $360 at 5% annually for 20 yrs = $12,331.01 (with monthly contributions of $30)

7. Answers may vary.

8. He was both a missionary and a pastor/teacher

9. False. Nowhere does scripture support this myth.

10. They need both. As you pray, you may be prompted to give, and as you give, you may be prompted to pray. For where your treasure is there will your heart be as well.

Lesson Practice 19.1

1. work for nothing but satisfaction; vested interest in work done properly

2. remember you are the boss; get recommendations; check that they are certified and insured; get estimates and bids in writing

3. painting, landscaping, washing cars and windows

4. instead of a bid, you pay them for their time (hourly wage) and provide the materials.

5. 400/460 = labor = 87%, 60/460 = materials = 13%

6. 2[2(9 x 8) + 2(12 x 8)] = 2[144 + 192] = 672 ft^2
672 ÷ 400 = just over 1.5, so 2 gallons of paint for walls

7. (9 x 12) = 108 ft^2, 1 quart if careful, but probably 2 quarts

8.   2(17 x 22)
  2(17 x 28)
+ 2(22 x 5 x 1/2)
  1,810 ft^2
19 squares of siding

9. 2(13 x 28) = 728 ft^2
8 squares of shingles

Lesson Practice 19.2

1. electrical, plumbing, heating

2. for clear communication and accountability

3. check references; clarify payment arrangements; ask if they charge by the job or the hour; ask when the clock starts if by the hour; if you have questions, ask

4. An estimate is a ball-park figure, while a bid is more of a specific contract.

5. 425/500 = labor = 85%
75/500 = materials = 15%

6. 2[2(15 x 8) + 2(24 x 8)] = 2[240 + 384] = 1,248 ft^2
1,248 ÷ 400 = little over 3, so 3 gal plus 1 qt if needed

SOLUTIONS

7. (15 x 24) = 360 ft^2, for 1 coat
   2 x 360 = 720 ft^2
   720 ÷ 400 = 1.8
   2 coats requires 2 gallons

8.   2(8 x 15)
      2(8 x 28)
    + 2(15 x 3 x 1/2)
    _____
      733 ft^2
    8 squares of siding

9. 12(9 x 28) = 504 ft^2
   6 squares of shingles

Lesson Review 19.3

1. 46 x $25 = $1,150 + $175 = $1,325
   20% of $1325 = $265
   $1,325 + $265 = $1,590

2. 48 x $25 = $1,200 + $148 = $1,348

3. $1590 – $148 (materials) =
   $1442 ÷ 48 (hrs he worked) =
   $30.04 per hour

4. $1590 – $1348 = $242

5. $85,000 x .03 =
     $2,550 for seller agent
   $85,000 x .03 =
     $2,550 for buying agent
   $2,550 + $2,550 = $5,100 for both

6. 2% transfer tax x $85,000 = $1,700
   $775 for Insurance
   $1,700 + $775 = $2,475

7. $85,000 – $7,925 = $77,075
   $5,100 (agents)
   $2,475 (taxes & insurance)
   + $350 (fees)
   _____
   $7,925

8. Praying brings God
   into the equation.

9. ask; ask

10. They pretended they were from a far
    away country and not one of the cities
    to be attacked by the Israelites.

Lesson Review 19.4

1. 20 x $19 = $380
   26 x $33 = $858
   _____
   $1,238

2. 19 – 14 = $5.00 per gal savings
   $5.00 x 20 gal = $100.00

3. 25 x $33 = $825 labor
   20 x $14 = $280 paint
   _____
   $1,105

4. $1,105 ÷ 4 = $276.25 per yr

5. 20 x $19 = $380
   25 x $33 = $825
   _____
   $1,205
   $1,205 ÷ 7 = $172.14 per yr

6. not usually

7.
   $$1\frac{1}{2} \text{ points} = 1\frac{1}{2}\% = .015$$

   .015 x $100,000 = $1,500.00

8. than to put confidence in man

9. Goodwill thrift stores,
   consignment shops.

10. yard sales; garage sales;
    pennysaver or advertising
    publications; local paper

Lesson Practice 20.1

1. free and accessible

2. only need the tool occasionally
   and can't afford the expense of
   purchasing it

3. 3.33 x $4.19 = $13.95

4. $13.95 + (.06 x 13.95) =
   $13.95 + .84 = $14.79

STEWARDSHIP

5. $10 \text{ ft} \times 6 \text{ ft} = 60 \text{ ft}^2$

6. $(4 \times \$1.99) + (3 \times \$5.89) =$
    $\$7.96 + \$17.67 = \$25.63$
    $\$25.63 + (\$25.63 \times .06) = \$27.17$

7. $(4 \times 1.25) + (3 \times 1.25) =$
    $5.00 + 3.75 = 8.75 \text{ yd}^2$

8. $(7.5 \times \$3.69) = \$27.68$
    $\$27.68 + (\$27.68 \times .06) = \$29.34$

9. $9 \times 12 = 108 \text{ ft}^2$
    $108 \text{ ft}^2 \div 9 = 12 \text{ yd}^2$

    $$\begin{array}{r} (12 \times \$15.00) \\ (12 \times \$5.40) \\ + (12 \times \$8.10) \\ \hline \$342.00 \end{array}$$

10. $\$15.00 + \$5.40 + \$8.10 = \$28.50$
    or $(\$342 \div 12 = \$28.50)$

Lesson Practice 20.2

1. tool breaking; you forgetting to re-turn it, owner needing it; bad feelings

2. If you will use it often, consider purchasing it.

3. $20 \text{ ft} \div 3 = 6.67 \text{ yd}$
    $6.67 \times \$4.29 = \$28.61$

4. $\$28.61 + (.055 \times \$28.61) =$
    $\$28.61 + \$1.57 = \$30.18$

5. 20 feet is 6 2/3 yd; 72 inches is 2 yd, 6 2/3 x 2 = 13 1/3 yd

6. $(5 \times \$1.89) + (5 \times \$5.89) =$
    $\$9.45 + \$29.45 = \$38.90$
    $\$38.90 + \$2.14 = \$41.04$

7. $(15 \times 4.5) + (15 \times 4.5) = 135 \text{ ft}^2$

8. $(\$3.79 \times 4.33) = \$16.41$
    $\$16.41 + \$1.03 = \$17.44$

9. $11 \times 15 = 165 \text{ ft}^2$
    $\$15.00 \div 9 = \$1.67 \text{ per ft}^2$
    $\$8.10 \div 9 = \$.90 \text{ per ft}^2$
    $\$5.40 \div 9 = \$.60 \text{ per ft}^2$

    $$\begin{array}{r} (165 \times 1.67) \\ (165 \times .90) \\ + (165 \times .60) \\ \hline \$523.05 \end{array}$$

10. $1.67 + .90 + .60 = \$3.17 \text{ per ft}^2$

Lesson Review 20.3

1. $3 + 2 = 5 \text{ events}$
    $5 \times 75.00 = \$375.00 \text{ to rent}$
    $\qquad\qquad\qquad \$250.00 \text{ to buy}$

    It will be more economical to buy.

2. $\$250 \div 75 = 3.33$

    He needs to wear it 4 times to do better than the price for renting a tux.

3. Answers may vary.

4. $\$1,000 \div \$29 = 34.48$
    so 35 times at the daily rate.
    $\$1,000 \div \$87 = 11.49$
    so 12 times at the weekly rate.

5. 2 walls $\qquad 12 \times 7\frac{1}{2} = 180$

    2 walls $\qquad 24 \times 7\frac{1}{2} = 360$

    $180 + 360 = 540 \text{ ft}^2 \text{ for 1 coat}$
    $1080 \text{ ft}^2 \text{ for 2 coats}$
    $1080 \div 400 = 2.7 \text{ gal}$
    You will need 3 gal for 2 coats

6. $12 \times 24 = 288 \text{ ft}^2$
    $288 \div 200 = 1.44 \text{ or}$
    1 gal and 2 qt

7. An amortization schedule on a loan is a detailed payment schedule showing the amount of interest and principal in each payment.

SOLUTIONS

8. discern—to perceive, apprehend, recognize, or comprehend.

9. Where no counsel is, the people fall: but in the multitude of counsellors there is safety. **Proverbs 11:14**

10. Answers may vary.

Lesson Review 20.4

1. $20 \times 14 = 280$; $280 \div 9 = 31.11$ yd^2
    Rounded to 32 yards
    Looking at the figure,
    if we don't use smaller pieces
    we would use $7 \times 5 = 35$ yards.

2. $280 \times \$.54 = \$151.20$

3. 35 yards (from figure) $\times \$7.50 = \$262.50$

4. $35 \times \$16.50 = \$577.50$
    $\$151.20 + \$262.50 + \$577.50 = \$991.20$

5. $70 \times 17 \times 2 = 2,380$ ft^2
    $2,380 \div 100 = 23.8$
    Rounded to 24 squares

6. $\$14.75 \times 24 = \$354.00$

7. Amortization Schedule

Pmnt#	Prin	Int	New Bal
1	358.32	125.00	24,641.68
2	360.11	123.21	24,281.57
3	361.91	121.41	23,919.66
4	363.72	119.60	23,555.93
5	365.54	117.78	23,190.39
6	367.37	115.95	22,823.03
7	369.20	114.12	22,453.82
8	371.05	112.27	22,082.77
9	372.91	110.41	21,709.86
10	374.77	108.55	21,335.09
11	376.64	106.68	20,958.45
12	378.53	104.79	20,579.92
13	380.42	102.90	20,199.50
14	382.32	101.00	19,817.18
15	384.23	99.09	19,432.94
16	386.16	97.16	19,046.79
17	388.09	95.23	18,658.70
18	390.03	93.29	18,268.68
19	391.98	91.34	17,876.70
20	393.94	89.38	17,482.76
21	395.91	87.41	17,086.86
22	397.89	85.43	16,688.97
23	399.88	83.44	16,289.10
24	401.87	81.45	15,887.22
25	403.88	79.44	15,483.34
26	405.90	77.42	15,077.43
27	407.93	75.39	14,669.50
28	409.97	73.35	14,259.53
29	412.02	71.30	13,847.51
30	414.08	69.24	13,433.42
31	416.15	67.17	13,017.27
32	418.23	65.09	12,599.04
33	420.32	63.00	12,178.71
34	422.43	60.89	11,756.29
35	424.54	58.78	11,331.75
36	426.66	56.66	10,905.09
37	428.79	54.53	10,476.29
38	430.94	52.38	10,045.35
39	433.09	50.23	9,612.26

STEWARDSHIP

40	435.26	48.06	9,177.00
41	437.44	45.89	8,739.57
42	439.62	43.70	8,299.94
43	441.82	41.50	7,858.12
44	444.03	39.29	7,414.09
45	446.25	37.07	6,967.84
46	448.48	34.84	6,519.36
47	450.72	32.60	6,068.64
48	452.98	30.34	5,615.66
49	455.24	28.08	5,160.42
50	457.52	25.80	4,702.90
51	459.81	23.51	4,243.10
52	462.10	21.22	3,780.99
53	464.42	18.90	3,316.58
54	466.74	16.58	2,849.84
55	469.07	14.25	2,380.77
56	471.42	11.90	1,909.35
57	473.77	9.55	1,435.58
58	476.14	7.18	959.44
59	478.52	4.80	480.92
60	480.92	2.40	0.00

Total interest paid: **$3999.20**

8. strong desire

9. Answers may vary.

10. Answers may vary.

Lesson Practice 21.1

1. $82.00

2. $\dfrac{12'}{1} \times \dfrac{60'}{1} \times \dfrac{1'}{2} = 360 \text{ ft}^3$

   $\dfrac{360 \text{ ft}^3}{1} \times \dfrac{1 \text{ yd}^3}{27 \text{ ft}^3} = 13.3 \text{ yd}^3$

3. $13.3 \div 11 = 1.2$, 2 truckloads

4. 3,500 concrete for a driveway,
   $83.50 x 13.3 = $1,110.55

5. $\dfrac{30'}{1} \times \dfrac{15'}{1} \times \dfrac{1'}{3} = 150 \text{ ft}^3 \times \dfrac{1 \text{ yd}^3}{27 \text{ ft}^3} =$
   5.56 yd³

   3,000 concrete for a patio,
   $82.00 x 5.56 = $455.92,
   1 truckload

6. $\dfrac{500}{3,500} = 14.3\%$

7. 20 cubic feet

8. $\dfrac{18 \text{ ton}}{1} \times \dfrac{1 \text{ yd}^3}{1.4 \text{ ton}} = 12.9 \text{ yd}^3$

9. $\dfrac{5 \text{ yd}^3}{1} \times \dfrac{1.4 \text{ ton}}{1 \text{ yd}^3} \times \dfrac{2,000 \text{ lbs}}{1 \text{ ton}} =$
   14,000 lb

10. $\dfrac{2,500 \text{ gal}}{1} \times \dfrac{1 \text{ ft}^3}{7.48 \text{ gal}} = 334.2 \text{ ft}^3$

Lesson Practice 21.2

1. $83.50/yd³

2. $\dfrac{12 \text{ ft}}{1} \times \dfrac{50 \text{ ft}}{1} \times \dfrac{5 \text{ ft}}{12} = 250 \text{ ft}^3$

   $\dfrac{250 \text{ ft}^3}{1} \times \dfrac{1 \text{ yd}^3}{27 \text{ ft}^3} = 9.3 \text{ yd}^3$

3. 1

4. 3,500 concrete for a driveway,
   $83.50 x 9.3 = $776.55

5. $$\frac{10 \text{ ft}}{1} \times \frac{15 \text{ ft}}{1} \times \frac{1 \text{ ft}}{4} =$$

   $$37.5 \text{ ft}^3 \times \frac{1 \text{ yd}^3}{27 \text{ ft}^3} = 1.39 \text{ yd}^3$$

   3,000 for a patio,
   82.00 x 1.39 = $113.98,
   1 truckload

6. $$\frac{1,200}{3,500} = 34.3\%$$

7. 2,000 ÷ 100 = 20 cubic feet

8. $$\frac{25 \text{ tons}}{1} \times \frac{1 \text{ yd}^3}{1.4 \text{ tons}} = 17.9 \text{ yd}^3$$

9. $$\frac{11 \text{ yd}^3}{1} \times \frac{1.4 \text{ tons}}{1 \text{ yd}^3} \times \frac{2,000 \text{ lbs}}{1 \text{ ton}} =$$

   30,800 lb

10. $$\frac{6,000 \text{ gal}}{1} \times \frac{1 \text{ ft}^3}{7.48 \text{ gal}} = 802.14 \text{ ft}^3$$

Lesson Review 21.3

1. $$\frac{1}{20} \times 5,280 = 264 \text{ ft}$$

   $$264 \text{ ft} \times 15 \text{ ft} \times 1 \text{ ft} = 3,960 \text{ ft}^3$$

   $$3,960 \div 27 \text{ ft}^3 = 146.67 \text{ yd}^3$$

   Rounded to 147 yd^3

2. 147 x 1,200 (sand) = 176,400 lbs
   147 x 1,800 (gravel) =
   264,600 lbs

3. 147 ÷ 11 = 13.36 -> rounded
   to 14 truckloads

4. 147 x 85.00 = $12,495.00

5. Answers may vary.

You still need a shovel. So whether you rent one for $6 or buy another one for yourself for $19.50, At the end of the day you have either spent $25.50 for renting a shovel and purchasing a new one for your friend or $39.00 for two shovels.

6. .68 x 9 = $6.12
   $6.00 per square yard is less than .68 per ft^2 ($6.12).

7. Find the square feet in your bedroom and multiply by .49 for padding, then determined how many square yards and multiply by $9.95. Add them together for your material expense.

8. He that believeth shall not make haste.

9. Only the good ones do. Generally they do not.

10. No.

Lesson Review 21.4

1. 10 ft x 23 ft x 4 in
   (4 in = 1/3 of 12 in = 1/3 of a ft)
   10 ft x 23 ft x 1/3 ft = 76.67 ft^3
   rounded to 77 ft^3

2. 77 ÷ 27 = 2.85 yd^3
   rounded to 3 yd^3

3. 3,000 grade since it is for a patio

4. 3 x 82.00 = $246.00

5. 24.95 ÷ 9 = $2.77 per ft^2

6. Answers may vary.

   Find the area of your living room and divide this by 9 ft^2 to find number of square yards, then multiply this answer to find the price for materials.

7. Answers may vary.
   $.85 x the area of your living room

8. It is usually a vacation resort or condominium that is divided up into shares of time. Each share is usually a week. You are buying a share of property.

9. No, unless you have completed the research needed to make an informed decision.

10. Answers may vary. It always does to me!

Lesson Practice 22.1

1. Area of Duct A = πr^2 = (3.14) 4^2 = 3.14 x 16 = 50.24 in^2
Area of Duct B = 6" x 8" = 48 in^2
More air will pass through Duct A.

2. Circumference of Duct A = $2\pi r$ = 2(3.14) 4 = 25.12 in
Perimeter of Duct B = 6" + 8" + 6" + 8" = 28 in

   Duct B uses more sheet metal.

3. V x A = W
120 x A = 60
A = 60 / 120 = .5 amps

4. 120 x 50 = W
120 x 50 = 6,000 watts

5. 120 x 20 x 80%= W
2,400 x .80 = 1,920 watts

6. 1,050 + (4 x 100) + (5 x 60) = 1,750 watts
120 x A = 1,750 watts
A = 1,750 / 120 = 14.58 amps
15 x 80% – 12 amps for safe capacity, so the answer is No.

7. 1,000 watts is a kilowatt, a kilowatt hour (KWH) is 1,000 watts for one hour

8.

Customer Charge:		8.00
200 KWH		
at 2.1930¢ per KWH		4.39
550 KWH		
at 1.9840¢ per KWH		10.91
750 KWH		
at 0.5640¢ per KWH		4.23
200 KWH		
at 1.3290¢ per KWH		2.66
550 KWH		
at 1.1780¢ per KWH		6.48
200 KWH		
at 5.1820¢ per KWH		10.36
550 KWH		
at 4.5540¢ per KWH		25.05

Total PPL

Electric Utilities Charges $72.08

Lesson Practice 22.2

1. Area of Duct A = πr^2 = (3.14) 3^2 =

   3.14 x 9 = 28.26 in^2

   Area of Duct B = 4.5" x 7" = 31.5 in^2

   More air will pass through Duct B.

2. Circumference of Duct A =

   $2\pi r$ = 2(3.14) 3 = 18.84 in

   Perimeter of Duct B =

   4.5" + 7" + 4.5" + 7" = 23 in

   Duct B uses the most sheet metal.

3. V x A = W
120 x A = 75
A = 75 / 120 = .625 amps

4. 120 x 60 = W
120 x 60 = 7,200 watts

5. 100 amp service

6. 120 x 30 = 3,600 watts
3,600 x 80% = 2,880 watts
for safe capacity

7. 500 + 800 + (5 x 100) =
1,800 watts
120 x A = 1,800 watts
A = 1,800 / 120 = 15 amps
20 x 80% = 16 amps for safe
capacity; the answer is yes.

8.

Customer Charge:	8.00
200 KWH	
at 2.1930¢ per KWH	4.39
600 KWH	
at 1.9840¢ per KWH	11.90
700 KWH	
at 1.8620¢ per KWH	13.03
1,500 KWH	
at 0.5640¢ per KWH	8.46
200 KWH	
at 1.3290¢ per KWH	2.66
600 KWH	
at 1.1780¢ per KWH	7.07
700 KWH	
at 1.0880¢ per KWH	7.62
200 KWH	
at 5.1820¢ per KWH	10.36
600 KWH	
at 4.5540¢ per KWH	27.32
700 KWH	
at 4.1780¢ per KWH	29.25
Total PPL Electric	
Utilities Charges	$130.06

Lesson Review 22.3

1. The area of Duct A = 5 in x 5 in =
  25 in^2

The area of Duct B = 4 in x 6 in =
  24 in^2

Duct A allows more air to pass
through it.

2. Perimeter Duct A =
5 in + 5 in + 5 in + 5 in = 20 in

Perimeter Duct B =
4 in + 6 in + 4 in + 6 in = 20 in
they the same amount of material

3.

$$V \times A = W$$

$$\frac{120}{120} \times A = \frac{40}{120}$$

$$A = .333$$

4. V x A = W
120 x 50 = W
6,000 = W
6,000 x .80 = 4,800 W

5. A cubic ft of water weighs 62.5 lb.
There are 27 ft^3 in a yd^3.
27 x 62.5 = 1,687.5 lb

6. 29,000 lb x 8.35 = 242,150 lb
242,150 ÷ 2,000 = 121.075 tons

7. 150 x 70% = 105
105 ÷ 62.5 = 1.68 ft^3

8. You can lead a sheep but you
have to drive a goat.

9. Colossians 3:15

10. God goes before his children
and leads them.

Lesson Review 22.4

1. Duct A has diameter of 5 inches
Radius is half diameter
so R = 2.5 inches
Duct A area =
π(2.5)^2 = (3.14)(6.25) = 19.625ft^2
Duct B = (4.5)^2 = 20.25 ft^2

Duct B

2. Circumference of Duct A =

πD = (3.14)(5) = 15.7 in

Perimeter of Duct B =

(4.5) x 4 = 18 in

Duct B

3. $V \times A = W$

$$\frac{120}{120} \cdot A = \frac{25}{120}$$

$$A = .21$$

4. $V \times A = W$

$120 \times 75 = W$

$9{,}000 = W$

$9{,}000 \times .80 = 7{,}200$ Watts

5. 5 gal $\times$ 8.35 = 41.75 lb

6 containers $\times$ 41.75 = 250.5 lb

6. 8.35 for a gal $\div$ 4 (quarts) =
    2.09 lb

7. $250 \div 62.5 = 4 \text{ ft}^3$

8. In a still small voice

9. His sheep

10. by the Spirit . . . sons of God.
    Romans 8:14

Lesson Practice 23.1

1. yard sales, garage sales, thrift shops

2. drink water and forgo dessert

3. $25.00 $\times$ .16 = $4.00

4. 1.5" x 3.5"

5. one by four

6. (.75" x 3) + (1.5" x 2) + 3.5" = 8.75"

7. Start with "two fifty-eight."
    Place two pennies in their hand
      and say "two sixty,"
    place one nickel in their hand
      and say "two sixty-five,"
    place one dime in their hand
      and say "two seventy-five,"
    place one quarter in their hand
      and say "three,"
    place two one-dollar bills
      in their hand and say "four - five."
    (There are other possibilities.)

8. Start with "six oh nine."
    lay out a penny
      and say "six ten,"
    lay out a nickel
      and say "six fifteen,"
    lay out a dime
      and say "six twenty-five,"
    lay out three quarters
      and say "six fifty, six
      seventy-five, seven,"
    lay out three one-dollar bills
    hand and say "eight, nine, ten."
    (There are other possibilities.)

Lesson Practice 23.2

1. newspaper ads; Goodwill;
    consignment shops

2. drinks and desserts

3. tip (15-16%) plus tax (5-6%) $\approx$ 20%

4. 1.5" x 5.5"

5. four by four

6. 3.5 + 5.5" + 7.25" + 7.25" = 23.5"

7. Start with "seventeen
      seventy-three,"
    place two pennies and say
      "seventeen seventy-five,"
    place one quarter and say
      "eighteen,"
    place two one-dollar bills and
      say "nineteen, twenty."
    (There are other possibilities.)

8. Start with "twenty-two twelve."
Place three pennies and say
 "twenty-two fifteen,"
place one dime and say
 "twenty-two twenty-five,"
place three quarters and say
 "twenty-two fifty, twenty-two
seventy-five, twenty-three,"
place two one-dollar bills and say
 "twenty-four, twenty-five,"
place one five-dollar bill,
 and say "thirty,"
place one twenty-dollar bill
 and say "fifty."
(There are other possibilities.)

Lesson Review 23.3

1. 42 x .05 = 2.10
42 x .17 = 7.14
42 + 2.10 + 7.14 = $51.24

2. $60 – $51.24 = $8.76

Start with
 "fifty-one twenty-four."
place one penny and say
 "fifty-one twenty-five,"
place another quarter and say
 "fifty-one fifty,"
place another quarter and say
 "fifty-one seventy-five,"
place another quarter and say
 "fifty-two,"
place three dollar bills and say
 "fifty-three, fifty-four,
 and fifty-five,"
Place a five-dollar bill and say
 "sixty."
(There are other possibilities.)

3. .75" x 3.5"

4. one by six

5. V x A = W
120 x 40 = W
4,800 = W
4,800 W x .80 = 3,840

6. V x A = W
120 x 20 = W
2,400 = W
2,400 x .80 = 1,920
1,920 - 500 (refrigerator) – 1,050
(toaster) = 370
370 ÷ 60 = 6 with 10 left so 6

7. Charges for PPL Electric Utilities

Residential Rate
Distribution charge:
 Customer Charge: 8.00

 200 KWH
  at 2.1930¢ per KWH 4.39

 600 KWH
  at 1.9840¢ per KWH 11.90

 200 KWH
  at 1.8620¢ per KWH 3.72
PA Tax Adj.
 Surcharge at .088% .03
Transmission Charge:
 1,000 KWH at 0.5640¢
  per KWH 5.64
Transition Charge:
 200 KWH at 1.3290¢
  per KWH 2.66
 600 KWH at 1.1780¢
  per KWH 7.07
 200 KWH at 1.0880¢
  per KWH 2.18
 PA Tax Adj. Surcharge
  at .064% .01
Generation Charge:
 Capacity and Energy
 200 KWH at 5.1820¢
  per KWH 10.36
 600 KWH at 4.5540¢
  per KWH 27.32
 200 KWH at 4.1780¢
  per KWH 8.36
 PA Tax Adj. Surcharge
  at .088% .02

Total PPL Electric
 Utilities Charges $91.67

8. differing weights
and differing measures

9. restoring or making compensation for loss, damage, or injury

10. both

Lesson Review 23.4

1. You won't need to pay a tip to a server.

2. Start with "five eighty-three." Place two pennies and say "five eighty-five," place a nickel and say "five ninety," place a dime and say "six" or "six dollars," place four dollar bills and say "seven, eight, nine, ten dollars," place a ten-dollar bill and say "twenty." (There are other possibilities.)

3. 3.5" x 5.5"

4. two by six

5. V x A = W
120 x 15 = W
1,800 = W
1,800 x .80 = 1,440 W

6. 1,440 – 1,050 (toaster) = 390 Watts
390 ÷ 40 = 9 with 30 extra

7. Answers may vary.

8. No, render to no man evil for evil.

9. as soon as the job has been completed

10. absolutely

Lesson Practice 24.1

1. haggling

2. in many countries outside of the US

3. Offer is what you would suggest to pay for an item, then the seller would give a higher figure which is their counteroffer.

4. A 2 x 6 wall is really 5 1/2" so the R value is 21.1 (Note: according to chart in lesson 24.)

5. For fiberglass the R value is 21

6. For polyurethane foam the R value is 44

7. 1.5" of foam is R-12, (1.5 x R-8) and 4" of cellulose is R-15.36 (4 x R-3.84) The total for the wall is R-27.36

8. 1.75" of foam is R-14, and 5.5" of fiberglass is R-21 The total for the wall is R-35

XC. Pink!!

Lesson Practice 24.2

1. shop around; pray; keep eyes and ears open

2. renting a truck for moving

3. wood flooring on skids for $5.00 and $10.00 casement and baseboard trim for $1.00 per stick

4. R-13.4

5. R-30

6. for foam, 8 x 3.5 = R-28

7. 1" of foam is R-8, and 2.5" of cellulose is R-9.6 (2.5 x R-3.84) The total for the wall is R-17.6

8. 3.5" of fiberglass is R-13, 5.75 of cellulose is R-22.08 (5.75 x R-3.84) The total for the 2 x 10 is R-35.08

XC. Yellow

Lesson Review 24.3

1. Answers may vary.

2. Answers may vary.

3. R-13

4. R-35.5

5.

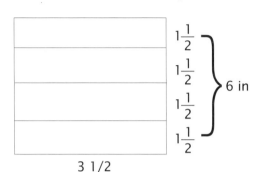

3 1/2

6. Start with "one forty-five."
Place a nickel and say "one fifty,"
place a quarter and say
"one seventy-five,"
place another quarter and
say "two" or "two dollars,"
place three dollar bills and say
"three, four, five."
(There are other possibilities.)

7. Start with "three sevety-three."
Place two pennies and
say "three seventy-five,"
place a quarter and say "four,"
place a dollar and say "five,"
place a five-dollar bill and say "ten"
(There are other possibilities.).

8. Yes, we all have been tempted.
Perhaps in some similar way in his time,
so was Jesus.

"For we have not a high priest that can
not be touched with the feeling of our
infirmities; but one that hath been in
all points tempted like as we are, yet
without sin." **Hebrews 4:15**

9. Temptation is not sin, yielding to
temptation is what leads to sin.
"But each man is tempted, when
he is drawn away by his own lust,
and enticed. Then the lust, when
it hath conceived, beareth sin;
and sin, when it is full grown,
bringeth forth death."
James 1:14-15 ASV

10. No. "He that is greedy of gain
troubleth his own house; but he
that hateth gifts shall live."
Proverbs 15:27

Lesson Review 24.4

1. Genesis 23

2. John Wanamaker

3. Answers may vary.

4. Answers may vary.

5.

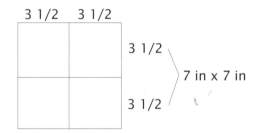

6. Start with "nine twenty."
Place a nickel and say "nine
twenty-five,"
place a quarter and say "nine fifty,"
place another quarter and
say "nine seventy-five,"
place another quarter and
say "ten,"
place a ten-dollar bill and
say "twenty."
(There are other possibilities.)

7. Start with "thirty-five eleven."
   Place four pennies and say
     "thirty-five twelve, thirteen,
     fourteen, and fifteen,"
   place a dime and say
     "thirty-five twenty-five,"
   place a quarter and say
     "thirty-five fifty,"
   place another quarter and say
     "thirty-five seventy-five,"
   place another quarter and say
     "thirty-six,"
   place four dollar bills and say
     "thirty-seven," "thirty-eight,"
     "thirty-nine," "forty,"
   place a ten-dollar bill and
     say "fifty."

   (There are other possibilities.)

8. He that hasteth to be rich hath an evil eye, and considereth not that poverty shall come upon him. ***Proverbs 28:22***

9. Put the price of the ticket you are tempted to buy back into your wallet.

   (There hath no temptation taken you but such as is common to man: but God is faithful, who will not suffer you to be tempted above that ye are able; but will with the temptation also make a way to escape, that ye may be able to bear it. ***1 Corinthians 10:13***)

10. The family suffers in not having their daily bread and the bread winner of the home suffers in knowing he is not providing for their basic needs.

Lesson Practice 25.1

1. 40 kph x .625 = 25 mph
2. 65 kph x .6 = 39 mph
3. 65 kph x .625 = 40.625 mph
4. 37° x 2 + 30° = 104°F

5. 37° x 9/5 + 32° = 98.6°
6. $50.00 US is about 37 euros
7.
$$\frac{50\ dollars}{1} \times \frac{.77\ euros}{1\ dollar} =$$
38.50 euros

8.
$$\frac{25\ euros}{1} \times \frac{1.29\ dollars}{1\ euro} =$$
32.25 dollars

XC. **Euro**pe

Lesson Practice 25.2

1. 55 mph x 1.6 ≈ 80 kmh
   since the ratio is 5 to 8, this is a little over 80 kmh.
2. 55 mph x 1.6 = 88 kmh
3. 70 kph X .6 = 42 mph,
   70 mph x .625 = 43.75 kph
4. 10° x 2 + 30° = 50°
5. 10° x 9/5 + 32° = 50°
6.
$$\frac{20\ dollars}{1} \times \frac{104.52\ yen}{1\ dollar} =$$
2,090.4 yen

7.
$$\frac{1,000\ yen}{1} \times \frac{1\ dollar}{104.52\ yen} =$$
9.57 dollars

8.
$$\frac{40\ dollars}{1} \times \frac{43.525\ rup}{1\ dollar} =$$
1,741 rupees

9.

$$\frac{800 \text{ rup}}{1} \times \frac{1 \text{ dollar}}{43.525 \text{ rup}} =$$

18.38 dollars

Lesson Review 25.3

1. 50 KPH x .6 = 30 MPH

2. 50 KPH x .625 = 31.25 MPH

3. 15°C doubled is 30°C + 30° = 60°F

4.

$$15° \left(\frac{9}{5} \right) + 32 = 27 + 32 = 59°F$$

5. R-74

6. 3 1/2 Foam = R-28

   2 x 8 is really 7 1/4 inches thick,

   minus 3 1/2 (foam) = 3 3/4 in

   3 3/4 in cellulose x 3.84 = R-14.4

   adding the foam and the cellulose

   R-28 + R-14.4 = R-42.4

7. 2 x 10 is really 9 1/4"
   inches thick, 1 inch of foam is R-8
   9 1/4 inches - 1 inch = 8 1/4 in
   8 1/4 in x 3.84 = 31.68
   adding the foam and the cellulose

   R-8 + R-31.68 = R-39.68

8. Seest thou a man diligent in his business? He shall stand before kings; he shall not stand before mean men.

   Proverbs 22:29

9. Not inclined to work, lazy, indolent.

10. Answers may vary.

Lesson Review 25.4

1. 80 KPH x .6 = 48 MPH

2. 80 KPH x .625 = 50 MPH

3. 25°C x 2 = 50° + 30° = 80°F

4.

$$\overset{5}{\cancel{25}}° \left(\frac{9}{\cancel{5}} \right) + 32 = 45 + 32 = 77°F$$

5. Answers may vary.

6. Answers may vary.

7. Answers may vary.

8. This expression is taken from the movie Where the Red Fern Grows. It means that in addition to faith and prayer we also have to be willing to supply diligence on our part in working towards an answer to prayer.

9. He was hungry. He needed to provide for the basic needs of his family.

10. Proverbs 16:26

Lesson Practice 26.1

1. 4 birdies is 4 x (–1),
   1 bogey (+1) = –4 + 1 = –3,
   36 – 3 = 33

2. 3 birdies is 3 x (–1),
   1 eagle is (–2),
   3 bogeys (+3)
   –3 – 2 + 3 = –2
   72 – 2 = 70

3.

4.

	1	2	3	4
Glenn	8	⊠	3 3	8 −
	20	36	42	50
Sarah	6 3	9 −	⊠	5 3
	9	18	36	44

5. $\dfrac{8}{22} = .3636 = .364$

6. $2 \times 4 + 2 \times 2 + 4 \times 1 = 16,$

$\dfrac{16}{22} = .7272 = .727$

7. $\dfrac{5 \times 9}{16} = \dfrac{45}{16} = 2.8125 = 2.81$

8. $\dfrac{16}{23} = .696 = .70$ winning

$\dfrac{7}{23} = .304 = .30$ losing

9. tie score

10. Roger, 29 to 26

Lesson Practice 26.2

1. 4 birdies is $4 \times (-1)$, $70 - 4 = 66$

2. 3 birdies is $3 \times (-1)$,
1 eagle is (-2), 4 bogeys $(+4)$,
1 double bogey $(+2)$,
$-3 - 2 + 4 + 2 = +1$
$72 + 1 = 73$

3. Sandy

4. Jessica

	1	2	3	4
Sandy	⊠	⊠	8⧄	7⊟
	28	48	65	72
Jessica	⊠	⊟8	5⧄	4⧄4
	18	26	40	48

5. $\dfrac{10}{29} = .3448 = .345$

6. $1 \times 4 + 3 \times 2 + 1 \times 3 + 5 \times 1 = 18,$
$\dfrac{18}{29} = .6206 = .621$

7. $\dfrac{3 \times 9}{24} = \dfrac{27}{24} = 1.125 = 1.13$

8. $\dfrac{14}{23} = .608 = .61$ winning

$\dfrac{9}{23} = .391 = .39$ losing

9. Roger, he won sets 1, 2, & 5

10. 3 and 5

Lesson Review 26.3

1. $7 \times (-1)$, $2 \times (+1)$
$-7 \quad\quad + 2 \quad = -5$
par is $71 - 5 = 66$

2. $6 \times (-1)$, $1 \times (-2)$, $2 \times (+1)$, $1 \times (+2)$
$-6 \quad\quad -2 \quad\quad +2 \quad\quad +2 = -4$
par is $72 - 4 = 68$

3. 36 Rich

4. 57 Scott

7⧄2	9⧄	8⧄1	⊠
9	27	36	
9⧄	⊠	3⧄6	9⧄
20	39	48	57

5. 30.00 US $\times .75 = 22.50$ in euros

6. $\dfrac{30.00 \text{ US}}{1} \times \dfrac{.77 \text{ Euros}}{1.00 \text{ US}} = 23.10$ Euros

7. 25 Euros $\times 1.3 = \$32.50$ US

8. 2 Corinthians 6:14

9. The believer is living for God and the unbeliever is living for self.

10. Yes. This will help with communication up front and later when there are disputes.

Lesson Review 26.4

1. 3 birdies +1 double bogey.
$9 - 4 = 5$ pars
$3 \times (-1) + 1 \times (+2)$
$-3 + 2 = -1$
$35 - 1 = 34$

2. 2 birdies + 11 pars = 13 holes
18 − 13 = 5 holes that are bogeys
2(−1) + 5(+1)
−2 + 5 = +3
72 + 3 = 75

3. 73

4. 50

John	⊠		⊠		9	/	5	4
	29		**49**		**64**		**73**	
Andrew	2	/	3	6	7	/	9	−
	13		**22**		**41**		**50**	

5. Estimating 50.00 US = 5,000 yen

6. $1{,}500 \text{ yen} \times \dfrac{1 \text{ dollar}}{104.52 \text{ yen}} =$

14.35 US dollars

7. $1{,}200 \text{ rupees} \times \dfrac{1 \text{ dollar}}{43.525 \text{ rupees}} =$

27.57 US dollars

8. Answers may vary.

9. servant

10. Yes. Recall Jack Whittaker, winner
of the 315 million dollar powerball
in 2002, who said, "And of course, once
they borrow money from you, you can't
be friends anymore."

Lesson Practice 27.1

1. 8 1/2" by 11"

2. legal

3. a ream of 17" x 22"
that weighs 20 pounds

4. 50# offset

5. 12 points in 1 pica

6. 18/72 = 1/4"

7. A4

8. basic

9. 8

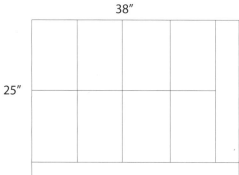

Lesson Practice 27.2

1. 8 1/2" by 5 1/2"

2. 500

3. 10 reams in one case

4. 3 x 500 + 300 = 4 reams

5. 24# pound

6. 6

7. 24/72 = 1/3"

8. cyan, magenta, yellow, black

9. 12

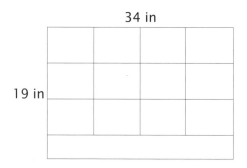

Lesson Review 27.3

1. 8 ½ in x 14 in

2. 24 lb, or 24#, is the weight of a ream of 17 in x 22 in paper.

3. 60# offset is similar to 24 in bond.

4. Bond paper has a watermark.

5. $\dfrac{10}{31} = .323$

6. ERA $= \dfrac{7 \times 9}{22} = \dfrac{63}{22} = 2.86$

7. Raphael won the match. They both won 26 games.

8. so that you will know whether you can complete the job once you have begun

9. a person who has made himself legally responsible for another

10. If you are surety or responsible for someone, you have committed to paying back and fulfilling their financial obligations if they are unable to do so themselves.

8. Collateral is something of value that is pledged to guarantee the price of the loan.

9. Do not become a guarantee or surety for someone. RUN, like a deer from a hunter or a bird from its captor.

10. because they don't have a good credit history and a bank will not loan them money unless you are their guarantee

Lesson Practice 28.1

1.

Course	% Grade	Letter Grade	Credit	Calc.
English	78	C	3	6
Algebra	72	C	3	6
Science	83	B	3	9
History	90	A	3	12
Latin	75	C	3	6
Phys. Ed.	99	A	1	4
			16	43

2. $\dfrac{43}{16} = 2.6975 = 2.69$

3.

Course	% Grade	Letter Grade	Credit	Calc.
English	78	C+	3	6.9
Algebra	72	C−	3	5.1
Science	83	B	3	9.0
History	90	A−	3	11.1
Latin	75	C	3	6.0
Phys. Ed.	99	A+	1	4.3
			16	42.4

$\dfrac{42.4}{16} = 2.65$

Lesson Review 27.4

1. 11 in x 17 in

2. a ream, or 500 sheets of basic size paper, 17 in x 22 in, 20# weighs 20 pounds.

3. 2600 ÷ 500 =
5 reams + 100 sheets or 5.2
We need 6 reams to finish the job.

4. 20# bond

5. $\dfrac{16}{40} = .400$

6. ERA $= \dfrac{1 \times 9}{16} = 0.56$

7. The last, or fifth set, was decided by a tie breaker.

4. $WC = 91.4 - (.474677 - .020425 \cdot V$
    $\qquad + .303107 \cdot \sqrt{V})(91.4 - T)$

    $WC = 91.4 - (.474677 - .020425 \cdot 10$
    $\qquad + .303107 \cdot 3.1623)(91.4 - 40)$

    $WC = 91.4 - (.474677 - .20425$
    $\qquad + .303107 \cdot 3.1623)(51.4)$

    $WC = 91.4 - (.270427 + .958515)(51.4)$

    $WC = 91.4 - 87.7464588 = 3.653542$

    rounds to 4°

5. If the temperature is 40°,
    and the velocity is 25 mph,
    the wind chill is 15°.

4. $WC = 91.4 - (.474677 - .020425 \cdot V$
    $\qquad + .303107 \cdot \sqrt{V})(91.4 - T)$

    $WC = 91.4 - (.474677 - .020425 \cdot 5$
    $\qquad + .303107 \cdot 2.2361)(91.4 - 30)$

    $WC = 91.4 - (.474677 - .102125$
    $\qquad + .303107 \cdot 2.2361)(61.4)$

    $WC = 91.4 - (.372552 + .677778)(61.4)$

    $WC = 91.4 - (64.490262) = 26.909738$

    rounds to 27°

5. If the temperature is 0°,
    and the velocity is 15 mph,
    the wind chill is -31°.

Lesson Practice 28.2

1.

Course	% Grade	Letter Grade	Credit	Calc.
English	88	B	3	9
Algebra	79	C	3	6
Science	73	C	3	6
History	85	B	3	9
Latin	92	A	3	12
Phys. Ed.	69	D	1	1
			16	43

2. $43 \div 16 = 2.6875 = 2.69$

3.

Course	% Grade	Letter Grade	Credit	Calc.
English	88	B+	3	9.9
Algebra	79	C+	3	6.9
Science	73	C	3	6.0
History	85	B	3	9.0
Latin	92	A-	3	11.1
Phys. Ed.	69	D+	1	1.3
			16	44.2

$44.2 \div 16 = 2.7625 = 2.76$

Lesson Practice 28.3

1.

Course	% Grade	Letter Grade	Credit	Calc.
Greek	92	A	3	12
Geometry	85	B	3	9
Origins	90	A	3	12
Geography	74	C	3	6
Bible	88	B	3	9
Disc Golf	79	C	1	2
			16	50

2. $50 \div 16 = 3.13$

3.

Course	% Grade	Letter Grade	Credit	Calc.
Greek	92	A-	3	11.1
Geometry	85	B	3	9.0
Origins	90	A-	3	11.1
Geography	74	C	3	6.0
Bible	88	B+	3	9.9
Disc Golf	79	C+	1	2.3
			16	49.4

$49.4 \div 16 = 3.09$

4. 1 credit for one hour
    in the classroom

5. $WC = 91.4 - (.474677 - .020425 \cdot 5$
$+ .303107 \cdot \sqrt{5})(91.4 - 40)$

$WC = 91.4 - (.474677 - .020425 \cdot 5$
$+ .303107 \cdot 2.2361)(91.4 - 40)$

$WC = 91.4 - (.474677 - .102125$
$+ .303107 \cdot 2.2361)(51.4)$

$WC = 91.4 - (.372552 + .677778)(51.4)$

$WC = 91.4 - (53.98696) = 37.41304$

rounds to 37°

6. −14°

7. Tentmaker

And because he was of the same trade, he abode with them, and they wrought, for by their trade they were tentmakers.

Acts 18:3

8. Aquila and Priscilla

And found a certain Jew named Aquila, born in Pontus, lately come from Italy, with his wife Priscilla; (because that Claudius had commanded all Jews to depart from Rome) and came unto them. *Acts 18:2*

9. They did not want to burden anyone.

For ye remember, brethren, our labor and travail; working night and day, that we might not burden any of you, we preached unto you the gospel of God.

1 Thessalonians 2:9, ASV

10. He took care of his own needs, and those that were with him. And in doing so, he was an example to them to help the weak, and how it is more blessed to give than to receive. You know that these hands of mine have worked to pay my own way, and I have even supplied the needs of those who were with me. And I have been a constant example of how you can help the poor by working hard. You should remember the words of the Lord Jesus: 'It is more blessed to give than to receive." *Acts 20:34-35*

Lesson Practice 28.4

1.

Course	% Grade	Letter Grade	Credit	Calc.
Greek	87	B	3	9
Geometry	91	A	3	12
Origins	95	A	3	12
Geography	82	B	3	9
Bible	93	A	3	12
Disc Golf	89	B	1	3
			16	57

2. $57 \div 16 = 3.56$

3.

Course	% Grade	Letter Grade	Credit	Calc.
Greek	87	B+	3	9.9
Geometry	91	A−	3	11.1
Origins	95	A	3	12.0
Geography	82	B−	3	8.1
Bible	93	A	3	12.0
Disc Golf	89	B+	1	3.3
			16	56.4

$56.4 \div 16 = 3.53$

4. 3 credits for three hours in the classroom

5. Find the wind chill for a temperature of 10° and wind speed, or velocity of 20 m/h

$WC = 91.4 - (.474677 - .020425 \cdot 20$
$+ .303107 \cdot \sqrt{20})(91.4 - 10)$

$WC = 91.4 - (.474677 - .020425 \cdot 20$
$+ .303107 \cdot 4.472136)(91.4 - 10)$

$WC = 91.4 - (.474677 - .4085$
$+ 1.355536)(81.4)$

$WC = 91.4 - (1.421713)(81.4)$

$WC = 91.4 - (115.727438) = -24.327438$

rounds to −24°

6. 4°

SOLUTIONS

7. The ability to paint helped Steve bless church members by working on their homes, and it helped him save the local church money by not having to hire a painter.

8. Steve was able to relate to others in the congregation who made a living working with their hands, he learned helpful skills, and he was able to influence his foreman towards God.

9. The poor and needy, her maidens, and her own household were recipients of the worthy woman's labors.

10. if you work quietly with your own hands, you will not be a burden on others and you will be able to help those who are in need.

   This should be your ambition: to live a quiet life, minding your own business and working with your hands, just as we commanded you before. As a result, people who are not Christians will respects the way you live, and you will not need to depend on others to meet your financial needs. *1 Thessalonians 4:11*

   Let him that stole steal no more: but rather let him labour, working with his hands the thing which is good, that he may have to give to him that needeth.

   Ephesians 4:28

Lesson Practice 29.1

1. bus
2. air
3. air; two hours and then I am there
4. quicker; two more days in Florida
5. air sickness; expense; parking at airport
6. scenery; relaxation

7. too long a trip to relax; almost 24 hours
8. Expedia, Orbitz, Travelocity, Sidestep No, discount airlines are not listed. They save money by not paying the search engines.
9. American Automobile Association
10. 2,734 miles
11. 1,446 miles
12. Chicago

Lesson Practice 29.2

1. car
2. train
3. car; gives you a chance to visit and stop and see friends along the way (answers will vary)
4. flexibility; restrooms; no rental car needed; expense
5. long trip; possible discomfort, depending on vehicle; traffic in Florida
6. cheap
7. diesel fumes; frequent stopping and starting
8. amtrak.com, greyhound.com
9. Alberta; (3,082 miles)
10. 2,533 miles; 5+ days
11. 993 miles
12. Sacramento; 3,042 miles

Lesson Practice 29.3

1. bus
2. car
3. Answers may vary.

For my family, which is just the three of us, flying is the best option. The cost is about the same and I get really tired driving all the way.

4. The bids you make on priceline are non-refundable and nontransferable.

5. St. Louis to Pittsburgh is 612 miles

6. There are 976 miles between Boston and Chicago.

7. Seattle is farthest from Atlanta; (2,734 miles)

8. by asking for it

9. Deuteronomy 8:12-14 tells us that the danger of having plenty of food is that our heart may be lifted up and we will forget the Lord our God.

10. Abram; Jacob

Lesson Practice 29.4

1. Answers may vary.

   Driving by car allows you the freedom to buy from a grocery store or restaurant.

2. Answers may vary; train or bus because of the limited options

3. Answers may vary.

   Air travel gets you there in a few hours instead of days.

4. air travel

5. Sacramento to Seattle there are 793 miles.

6. From Atlanta to Calgary there are 2,415 miles.

7. There are only 554 miles between New Orleans and Dallas.

8. The blessing of the Lord

9. God at creation

10. Work six, rest one.

Lesson Practice 30.1

1. United States Postal Service

2. red, white, and blue

3. overnight to most areas, $27.30 or $29.95

4. two days at the quickest, possibly three; $9.85 or $12.50

5. $2.20

6. Yes, $.45 for Express & Priority, $.55 for Parcel Post

7. 1.5 miles for me; this will be different for you

8. NW is northwest, the degree equivalent is 315°

9. South southwest, the degree equivalent is 202.5°

10. 90°

Lesson Practice 30.2

1. United Parcel Service

2. brown

3. ground shipping

4. 3 day guaranteed delivery

5. free up to 100.00

6. no fee for UPS

7. Answers may vary.

8. SW is southwest; the degree equivalent is 225°

9. South southeast; the degree equivalent is 157.5°

10. 135°

Lesson Practice 30.3

1. $63.30

2. $33.75

3. $2.20

4. $.55

5. WSW, 247.5°

6. ENE, East Northeast

7. 135°

8. 1 of 10 is 10%, Luke 17:17

9. be ye thankful

10. Every good gift and every perfect gift is from above, coming down from the Father of lights, with whom can be no variation, neither shadow that is cast by turning.

   James 1:17 ASV

Lesson Practice 30.4

1. not usually, but check to make sure

2. $21.11

3. no

4. 5# is $10.10, 25# is $21.11
   $21.11 – 10.10 = $11.01 for 20#
   or $.55 per pound.

5. ESE is East Southeast, 112.5°

6. NNW, North Northwest

7. 225° (SW) – 112.5° (ESE) = 112.5° difference

8. being a good steward of God's resources.

9. Answers may vary.
   (For Steve it was finishing this last lesson.)

10. Answers may vary.

Test Solutions

Test 1

1. $12.80 x 38 = $486.40

2. $12.80 x 40 = $512.00
   12.80 x 1.5 (overtime) x 5 = $96.00
   $512 + $96 = $608

3. $12.80 x 40 = $512.00
   $12.80 x 1.5 x 2.5 = $48.00
   $512 + $48 = $560.00
   week 1 + week 2 + week 3 =
   $486.40 + $608.00 + $560.00 =
   $1,654.40

   38 + 45 + 42.50 = 125.50
   $1,654.40 ÷ 125.50 = $13.18/hr

4. 13.25 x 2,000 = $26,500.00

5. $39,000 ÷ 2,000 = $19.50

6. 180,000 dinars x .03 = 5,400 dinars

7. .25 x 218 goats = 54.50 dinars

8. $160.00 x .35 = $56.00

9. Proverbs

10. faithful

Test 2

1. $23.80 x .06 = $1.43
   $23.80 + $1.43 = $25.23

2. $23.80 x .17 = $4.05

3. $23.80 + $1.43 + $4.05 =
   $29.28 — > $30

4. By April 13th—WIthin 10 days.

5. 736.00 x .02 = 14.72

6. 25 days or by April 28th

7. $1,895.00 - 5% x $1,895.00 =
   $1,895.00 - $94.75 = $1,800.25

8. $1,895.00 + 1% x $1,895.00 =
   $1,895.00 + $18.95 = $1,913.95

9. love

10. two masters

Test 3

1. $37,440.00 ÷ 52 = $720.00

2. $720 x .085   = $61.20
   $720 x .0307 = $22.10

3. $720 x .0165 = $11.88
   $720 x .062   = $44.64

4. $720 x .0145 = $10.44
   $720 x .0009 = $ .65

5.   61.20
        22.10
        11.88
        44.64
        10.44
   +   .65
   ─────────
   $150.91

6. 720 - 150.91 = $569.09

7. 569.09 ÷ 40 = $14.23 per hour

8. 720.00 - (44.64 + 10.44) = $664.92
   664.92 x .10 = $66.49

9. giving or unselfish

10. selfish

Test 4

1. holding your money, saving your
   money, moving your money,
   loaning money.

2. yours, mine, and our neighbors'

3. mortgage

4. placing your money in the bank

5. Automated Teller Machine

6. Home equity is the amount of your home that has already been paid. It is the total of the principal payments on your mortgage.

7. Collateral is something of value comparable to the monetary worth of your loan.

8. A savings account.

9. Fill in the blanks. Be ye free from the love of money; content with such things as ye have: for himself hath said, I will in no wise fail thee, neither will I in any wise forsake thee.

   Hebrews 13:5, ASV

10. Fill in the blank. The opposite of covetousness is contentment.

Test 5

1. Joseph B. Unit

2. Christian Freedom International

3. $275.00, in numerals to the far right of the check and in the line directly below the numerals, written out with words.

4. 2981

5. 07893456

6. below the address of the bank and in the lower left hand corner with computer script.

7. 12 Main St., Goodtown, PA 15000

8. To remind you of the purpose of the check—in this case, that it is for the resettlement of the Karen people

9. David; own heart

10. There will your heart be also.
    Luke 12:34

Test 6

1. .08 x $3,650.00 = $292.00.
   $3,650.00 + $292.00 = $3,942.00

2. 8% divided into 4 quarters is 2% or .02.
   $3,650.00 x .02 = $73.00
   $3,650.00 + $73.00 = $3,723.00
   $3,723.00 x .02 = $74.46
   $3,723.00 + $74.46 = $3,797.46
   $3,797.46 x .02 = $75.95
   $3,797.46 + $75.95 = $3,873.41
   $3,873.41 x .02 = $77.47
   $3,873.41 + $77.47 = $3,950.88

3. 8% divided by 2 for semiannual is 4% or .04.
   $3,650.00 x .04 = $146.00
   $3,650.00 + $146.00 = $3,796.00
   $3,796.00 x .04 = $151.84
   $3,796.00 + $151.84 = $3,947.84

4. $3,950.88 is the greatest return of the three so #2.

5. .10 x $5,000.00 = $500.00.
   $5,000.00 + $500.00 = $5,500.00

6. 10% divided into 4 quarters is 2.5% or .025.
   $5,000.00 x .025 = $125.00
   $5,000.00 + $125.00 = $5,125.00
   $5,125.00 x .025 = $128.13
   $5,125.00 + $128.13 = $5,253.13
   $5,253.13 x .025 = $131.33
   $5,253.13 + $131.33 = $5,384.46
   $5,384.46 x .025 = $134.61
   $5,384.46 + $134.61 = $5,519.07

7. 10% divided into 2 for semiannual is 5% or .05.
   $5,000.00 x .05 = $250.00
   $5,000.00 + $250.00 = $5,250.00
   $5,250.00 x .05 = $262.50
   $5,250.00 + $262.50 = $5,512.50

8. $5,519.07 is the greatest return of the three so #6.

STEWARDSHIP

9. good, good works
10. himself, God

10. what you do

Test 7

1. Certificate of Deposit
2. Individual Retirement Account
3. You pay taxes now and not when you withdraw your retirement funds.
4. risk
5. monthly
6. The approximate value of an initial investment. 6 x 12 years = 72, and $7,777.00 x 2 = $15,554.00
7. 250.00 x 12 months x 20 years = $60,000.00
8. $147,255.10 – $60,000.00 = $87,255.10
9. God promises to meet our needs.
10. 10%

Test 8

1. money that is coming in to you
2. their salary or payment for the work they perform
3. savings, emergencies, future needs, help for others
4. someone that sets aside funds for a specific purpose in an envelope
5. money that is spent; answers will vary
6. This exercise will reveal spending habits and patterns and provide a foundation for a budget.
7. Crown
8. housing
9. do all to the glory of God

Test 9

1. The retail price is $5.95.
2. WP of 5.95 is 3.10
WP = 3.10 / 5.95 = .52 = 52%
3. $105.00 – $58.00 = $47.00
4. Wp of $105.00 = $47.00
WP = $47.00 / $105.00 = .45 = 45%
5. Wp of $58.00 = $47.00
WP = $47.00 / $58.00 = .81 = 81%
6. $1.45 – $1.05 = .40 markup
Wp of $1.45 = $.40
WP = $.40 / $1.45 = .28 = 28%
7. The volume of eggs sold is much higher than the number of sandals sold during the same time period.
8. 60% of $15.97 is .60 x $15.97 = $9.58
$15.97 – $9.58 = $6.39 or you could say
100% – 60% = 40% and 40% of $15.97
is .40 x $15.97 = $6.39
9. In their home or personal estate
10. A pastor or Christian worker is worthy of pay for his labors.

Test 10

1. It is convenient to just use "plastic" instead of carrying cash. You may receive a rebate on purchases or perks like free airline tickets.
2. You can spend only what you have in your checking account at the bank.
3. Annual Percentage Rate
Divide the APR by 12 for 12 months.
4. 18 ÷ 12 = 1 1/2%
5. 1 1/4 x 12 = 15%

6.

Payment	Monthly Payment	Principal Paid	Interest	Balance
1	23.96	16.76	7.20	463.24
2	23.96	17.02	6.95	446.22
3	23.96	17.27	6.69	428.95

7. $51.05

8. $20.84

9. When you are performing work for someone you should be thinking that you will do it for them as you would want someone to do the same work for you.

10. Six

Test 11

1. $7.77 ÷ 12 = $.65, $.79, $2.59 ÷ 3 = $.86

2. 4 x $.30 = $1.20,
10 x $.30 = $3.00, 20 x $.30 = $6.00

3. 3 x $.79 = $2.37 + $1.20 = $3.57
and $3.57 ÷ 3 = $1.19 per can

3 for $2.59 + $3.00 = $5.59
and $5.59 ÷ 3 = $1.86 per can

12 for $7.77 + $6.00 = $13.77
and $13.77 ÷ 12 = $1.15 per can

4. convenience store wins, since it is closer, quicker, and a great price

5. 29.99 ÷ 10 = $2.99 per ream
7.99 ÷ 2 = $4.00 per ream

6. 6 x $.30 = $1.80 and 8 x $.30 = $2.40 (not much difference)

7. $7.99 + $1.80 = $9.79 ÷ 2 = $4.90 per ream at the pharmacy

$29.99 + $2.40 = $32.39 ÷ 10 = $3.24 per ream at the office store

8. Isaac went to the office store because the quality of the paper at the pharmacy was okay for copy purposes but not for a term paper. The cost was better and he could always use the paper in the future.

9. Proverbs 31—the worthy woman

10. yes, absolutely

Test 12

1.

PLAN A	100 min	250 min	500 min
5¢ per min	5.00	12.50	25.00
3.95 per mo.	3.95	3.95	3.95
Price per min	9.0¢	6.6¢	5.8¢
		(16.45 ÷ 250)	(28.95 ÷ 500)

PLAN B	100 min	250 min	500 min
7¢ per min	7.00	17.50	35.00
0.00 per mo.	0.00	0.00	00.00
Price per min	7¢	7¢	7¢

2. Plan A $150 \times .05 + 3.95 =$
7.50 + 3.95 = $11.45

Plan B $150 \times .07 =$
$10.50 This is the best.

3. Plan A $600 \times \$.05 + \$3.95 =$
$30.00 + $3.95 = $33.95
This is the best.

Plan B $600 \times \$.07 = \$42.00$

4. $.05M + 3.95 = .07M$
$100 (.05M + 3.95 = .07M) =$
$5M + 395 = 7M$

Subtract 2M from both sides
$395 = 2M$

Divide both sides by 2 and
$M = 197.5$ minutes
For fewer than this number, as for 150 minutes, Plan B is the best, but more than 198 minutes Plan A is the victor.

5.

	100 min	250 min	500 min
$30 mo. fee	30.00	30.00	30.00
45¢ add. min.	0.00	0.00	250 x .45 =112.50
Price per min.	30¢	12¢	28.5¢

6.

	100 min	250 min	500 min
$50 mon. fee	50.00	50.00	50.00
25¢ add. min.	0.00	0.00	0.00
Price per min.	50¢	20¢	10¢

7. Plan A 30.00 (first 250 minutes)
+ 150 (400 – 250) x .45
30.00 + 67.50 = 97.50 for 400 min

Plan B is 50.00 for 400 minutes as it is less than the 500 anytime minutes in the plan.

For 400 minutes Plan B is the best deal.

8. Plan A—30.00 since 200 is less than the 250 anytime minutes

Plan B—50.00, as 200 is less than the 500 anytime minutes in the plan
For 200 minutes Plan A is the clear choice.

9. Yes.

Be not therefore anxious, saying, What shall we eat? or, What shall we drink? or, Wherewithal shall we be clothed? For after all these things do the Gentiles seek; for your heavenly Father knoweth that ye have need of all these things. But seek ye first his kingdom, and his righteousness; and all these things shall be added unto you.
Matthew 6:31-33 ASV

10. Rome

Test 13

1. Value is intangible. It includes customer service and high quality. Price is dollars and cents.

2. A trained staff, which can share information, knowledge, and give great customer service.

3. usually a higher price and limited inventory

4. 1 MB is 1,024 KB

5. 1 Gigabyte

6. A warranty doesn't last for the life of the product, as does a lifetime guarantee. A warranty is the pledge of the company to stand behind their product.

7. a large stock of inventory and lower prices

8. a limited variety within a product line; distance to travel

9. One method that some use to help them remember to save is to set aside ten percent for future needs at the same time that they return 10 percent to God.

10. physical cities

Test 14

1. appreciation

2. A lease is an extended rental agreement.

3. $16,810 – $9,090 = $7,720

4. Yes, very much so.

5. A. Interest rate

B. Down payment

C. Cost of the vehicle (which can change when you are financing it)

D. Insurance requirements (since you are renting their car until it is paid for, they may require additional coverage)

E. Length of the loan

F. Rebate details

G. Other requirements that you need to be aware of, for their loan.

H. Potential charges if you finance it through your local bank!

6. $2,886.58

7. $16,800.00 + $2,886.58 = $19,686.58

8. $12,400.00

9. *Luke 12:34* For where your treasure is there will your heart be also.

10. Your income and your outgo, or expenses.

Test 15

1. 375 ÷ 18.5 = 20.27 mpg

2. 18.5 x $3.09 = $57.17

3. $57.17 ÷ 375 = .15 per mile

4. Gasoline is $1,600.00 and depreciation is $1,930.00.

5. 1,600.00 + 1,930.00 = 3530.00 ÷ 15,000 = .235 or

   .24 per mile

6. 4,985.00 ÷ 15,000 = .33 per mile

7. You have access to a lot of information about the cost of the car and you have several sites available for purchasing a new or used car, so much more selection.

8. You can't sit in the vehicle and take it for a test drive. It is difficult to take it back to the garage and return it if there are problems. If you buy it out of state it may be difficult or an added expense to have it delivered to you.

9. Because we have no promise of tomorrow.

   Go to now, ye that say, To day or to morrow we will go into such a city, and continue there a year, and buy and sell, and get gain: Whereas ye know not what shall be on the morrow.

   For what is your life? It is even a vapour, that appeareth for a little time, and then vanisheth away. For that ye ought to say, If the Lord will, we shall live, and do this, or that.

   James 4:13-15

10. tomorrow

Test 16

1. $\frac{3}{4} = \frac{12}{16}$

   $\frac{12}{16} + \frac{1}{16} = \frac{13}{16}$

2. $\frac{3}{16} \bigcirc \frac{3}{8} \longrightarrow \frac{3}{16} \bigotimes \frac{6}{16}$

3. The width is 190 mm.

4. 75% x 190 mm = 142.5 mm

5. $142.5 \text{ mm} \times \frac{.4 \text{ in}}{10 \text{ mm}} = 5.7 \text{ in}$

6. $15 \text{ in} \times \frac{10 \text{ mm}}{.4 \text{ in}} = 375 \text{ mm}$, which is the diameter of the rim

   142.5 mm + 142.5 mm + 375 mm = 660 mm

   5.7 in + 5.7 in + 15 in = 26.4 in

7. $R \cdot T = D$

   $55 \frac{\text{miles}}{\text{hour}} = 55 \frac{\text{mi}}{\text{hr}}$ and $\frac{1}{55 \frac{\text{mi}}{\text{hr}}} = \frac{1 \text{ hr}}{55 \text{ mi}}$

   $55 \frac{\text{mi}}{\text{hr}} \cdot T = 10 \text{ mi}$

$$\frac{\cancel{X}\,\cancel{hr}}{55\,\cancel{mi}} \cdot \frac{55\,\cancel{mi}}{\cancel{X}\,\cancel{hr}} \cdot T = 10mi \cdot \frac{1\ hr}{55\ mi}$$

$$T = 10mi \cdot \frac{1\ hr}{55\ mi} = \frac{10\ hr}{55\ mi} \cdot \frac{60\ min}{1\ hr}$$

$$= 10.91\ min$$

8. $R \cdot T = D$
   $R \cdot 52\ sec = 1mi$
   $R \cdot 52\ sec = (60\ mph)(60\ sec) = 3600$
   $R = \dfrac{(60\ mph)(60\ \cancel{sec})}{52\ \cancel{sec}}$
   $R = 69.23\ mph$

9. This early habit of giving will help to make the habit of giving when you are older.

10. Giving regularly helps ministries have the funds they need to function efficiently and effectively throughout the year.

Test 17

1. An insurance premium is the fee you pay to an insurance agency in exchange for their reimbursing your losses and expenses.

2. $800.00 x 55% =
   $800.00 x .55 = $440.00

3. Two other types of auto insurance are comprehensive and collision.

4. Deductible is what you pay first before the insurance agency begins to fulfill their obligation and pay the expenses and losses.

5. Teen drivers are more likely statistically to have an accident than older, more experienced drivers.

6. Carry a high deductible on your home since you are not driving it around on the roads at 60 mph and you are not as prone to need insurance as on a car.

7. Sharing is members each bearing one another's burdens and helping shoulder the needs of each other.

8. Term life insurance is a rental of an insurance policy for a specific length of time.

9. They can expect to receive who have been practicing giving.

10. And this is the confidence that we have toward him, that if we ask anything according to his will he hears us.

   1 John 5:14, ESV

Test 18

1. If you are renting, the landlord has the responsibility for the house. He not only takes care of the property, but as the owner pays the taxes as well.

2. If you live in a home for several years and then move, you don't have any money or equity to show for all of the monthly payments you have made. You had a place to stay, but after spending thousands of dollars, the money is gone and you have nothing to show for it.

3. A lien is the right of a creditor to collect what he is owed from the sale of an asset, in this case real estate.

4. Title insurance insures that there are no liens on the property you are purchasing, and if there are, they will be covered by your insurance policy.

5. 2 1/2% is the same as 2 1/2 points.

6. Owning your own home is investing for the future. If you move, you should be able to sell your house and not only recover what you have invested into your home but make a profit as well.

7. A standard plus 50 means you are making the standard monthly payment and then adding an additional $50.00 to be applied towards the remaining principal.

8. By making this additional payment you will be able to save on the total interest on the mortgage and pay off the loan sooner, saving even more money.

9. This might be your needy neighbor, a poor individual, widows or orphans, and Christian workers at home and abroad.

10. Pure, fatherless, widows

Test 19

1. Do-it-yourselfers save money and have the satisfaction of doing the job themselves.

2. Time and materials means you pay the worker exactly what they earn for the amount of time they spend times an hourly wage, and for the materials needed to accomplish their job.

3. $10 \times 7.5 + 14 \times 7.5 + 10 \times 7.5 + 14 \times 7.5 = 75 + 105 + 75 + 105 = 360$ ft^2
360 ft^2 $\times$ 2 coats = 720 ft^2

   If there are 400 ft^2 per gallon, then $720 \div 400 = 1.8$, so I would suggest 2 gallons.

4. $10 \times 14 = 140$ ft^2
   If there are 400 ft^2 per gallon, then $140 \div 400 = .35$. You will need at least 2 quarts of paint. But depending on the cost of a gallon, you may want to get a full gallon. Since it is ceiling paint and probably white, you can use what is left over in other rooms.

5. $28 \times 15 + 28 \times 15 + 34 \times 15 + 34 \times 15 = 420 + 420 + 510 + 510 = 1,860$ ft^2

At 100 ft^2 per square, $1,860 \div 100 = 18.6$. You will need 19 squares. But you may have enough just buying 17 squares, depending on how many windows and door openings there are on the house.

6. $34 \times 16 \times 2 = 1,088$ ft^2
At 100 ft^2 per square, $1,088 \div 100 = 10.88$. You will need 11 squares.

7. Writing out what work is to be done and how it is to be accomplished clarifies expectations and promotes more effective communication. In case of a bid, your written agreement is a form of contract.

8. An estimate is an educated guess. I used to call them guesstimates. A bid is a firm price.

9. When you pray and ask God for his assistance, you involve Him in the process.

10. Be careful for nothing; but in every thing by prayer and supplication with thanksgiving let your requests be made known unto God.

Philippians 4:6

Test 20

1. When you borrow a tool from a neighbor it is free, and you may have easy access to it.

2. Before purchasing a tool you would need to consider the cost of the tool and whether you will have need of it in the future.

3. The factors for determining the wisdom of renting are the same as in #2. If you are not going to regularly use the tool or machine, and if it is an expensive item, then renting is preferable.

4. 16 ft ÷ 3 (feet per yard) = 5 1/3 yards
5 1/3 x $4.29 = $22.88.
$22.88 x .06 (6% tax) = $1.37
$22.88 + $1.37 = $24.25

5. 16 ft x 5 ft (60 in) = 80 ft^2

6. 2 x $2.29 + 2 x $5.89 =
$4.58 + $11.78 = $16.36
$16.36 x .05 (5% tax) = $.82
$16.36 + $.82 = $17.18

7.

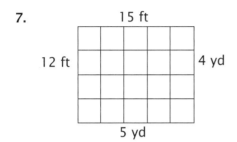

12 ft x 15 ft = 180 ft^2 180 ft^2 x $.90 = $162.00 for padding

4 yd x 5 yd = 20 yd^2
20 yd^2 x $12.50 = $250.00 for carpet

12 ft x 15 ft = 180 ft^2

180 ft^2 x $.60 = $108.00 for installation
$162.00 + $250.00 + $108.00 = $520.00

8. $520.00 ÷ 20 = $26.00

9. Lust is a synonym for strong desire.

10. multitude, counselors

2. Since there are 11 yards per truckload, you will need two trucks.

3. 12.5 x $83.50 = $1,043.75

4. $\dfrac{4\ in}{12\ in} = \dfrac{1\ ft}{3}$

70 ft x 3 ft x $\dfrac{1}{3\ ft}$ = 70 ft^3

70 ft^3 ÷ 27 (cubic feet per yard)
= 2.59 yd^3, so this will be 1 truckload.

5. 2.59 x $82.00 = $212.38

6. 1,200 ÷ 3,500 = .34 or 34%

7. Since 1.4 tons of gravel is the same as 1 cubic yard:

$\dfrac{1.4\ tons}{1\ yd^3}$ = 1 and $\dfrac{1\ yd^3}{1.4\ tons}$ = 1

10 tons x $\dfrac{1\ yd^3}{1.4\ tons}$ = 7.14 yd^3

8. 1 ft^3 of water = 7.48 gallons and there are 27 ft^3 of water in 1 yd^3
27 ft^3 times 7.48 gallons =
201.96 gal in a yd^3
1 gallon of water weighs 8.35 lb

8.35 lbs times 201.96 gal =

1,686.366 or 1,686.37 lb

9. Don't move quickly to make a purchase until you have done the necessary research to make an informed decision.

10. believes, haste

Test 21

1. $\dfrac{9}{12} = \dfrac{3}{4}$

10 ft x 45 ft x $\dfrac{3\ ft}{4}$ = 337.5 ft^3

337.5 ft^3 ÷ 27(cubic feet per yard)

= 12.5 yd^3

Test 22

1. If the diameter is 6.5 inches, the radius is one half of that or 3.25 inches

   Duct A = Area of the Circle = πr^2
   $$= (3.14)(3.25)^2$$
   $$= 33.16625 = 33.17 \text{ in}^2$$

   Duct B = Area of the Square
   $$= (5.5 \text{ inches})^2 = 30.25 \text{ in}^2$$

   Duct A will let more air pass through.

2. Duct A = Circumference of the Circle
   $$= \pi D = (3.14)(6.5) = 20.41 \text{ in}$$

   Duct B = Perimeter of the Square
   $$= (5.5 \text{ inches}) \times 4 = 22 \text{ in}$$

   Duct B will use more sheet metal.

3. $V \cdot A = W$

4. $\dfrac{120}{120} \cdot A = \dfrac{75}{120}$

   $A = \dfrac{75}{120}$

   Amps = .625

5. $V \cdot A = W$

   $120 \cdot 40 = W$

   $4,800 = \text{Watts}$

6. $V \cdot A = W$

   $120 \cdot 25 = W$

   $3,000 = \text{Watts}$

   $W \cdot 80\%$ is safe capacity.

   $3,000 \text{ W} \cdot .80 = 2,400 \text{ watts}$

7.
Toaster	1,050 watts
Microwave	800 watts
2 – 100 w bulbs	200 watts
8 – 60 w bulbs	480 watts
	2,530 watts

   $120 \cdot 20 = 2,400 \text{ watts}$
   $2,400 \text{ W} \cdot .80 = 1,920 \text{ watts}$
   so 2,530 watts would be too much

8. KWH = 1 Kilowatt hour

9. God leads His people as a good shepherd. You can lead sheep but you have to drive goats.

10. peace, thankful

Test 23

1. A few great places to find bargains are garage sales, yard sales, estate sales, classified ads in the newspaper, and penny saver supplements in the newspaper.

2. To save money at a restaurant, drink water and don't purchase dessert.

3. $1\frac{1}{2}$ in x $3\frac{1}{2}$ in

4. 4 x 4

5. $\frac{3}{4}$ in + $\frac{3}{4}$ in + $1\frac{1}{2}$ in + $1\frac{1}{2}$ in + $1\frac{1}{2}$ in + $3\frac{1}{2}$ in =

   $9\frac{1}{2}$ in

6. When the board is rough cut, it is 1 in by 4 inches, but after being finished and planed it has final dimensions of 3/4 inch by 3 1/2 inches.

7. Start with "seven eleven."
   Place four pennies and say "seven twelve, thirteen, fourteen, fifteen,"
   place a dime and say "seven twenty-five,"
   place a quarter and say "seven fifty,"
   place another quarter and say "seven seventy-five,"
   place another quarter and say "eight,"
   place two dollar bills and say "nine, ten."

8. The additional 20% comes from tax (5-7%) and the tip (15-16%).

9. Do unto others as you would have others do unto you.

10. This is absolutely the best way to do business.

Test 24

1. Haggling

2. You, as the customer, make an initial offer or new suggestion of a price you are wanting to pay for an item or a service. The vendor then has the opportunity to counter or respond with a different amount that he is willing to take for his goods or service.
If this continues, then all offers will be alternative or counteroffers.

3. R stands for thermal resistance or the resistance to heat flow. R-value is a measure of how effective your insulation is at keeping heat in your home.

4. Polyurethane foam insulation

5. A 2 x 4 wall is 3 1/2" deep.
3.5 x 3.84 = R-13.44

6. A 2 x 6 wall is 5 1/2" deep.
According to the information above, R-21.

7. A 2 x 4 wall cavity is 3 1/2" deep.
3.5 x 8.0 = R-28

8. A 2 x 8 wall is 7 1/4" deep.
7 1/4" minus 1 1/4" for foam is
6" for cellulose. 1.25 x 8.0 = R-10 and
6.0 x 3.84 = R-23.04
R-10 plus R-23.04 = R-33.04

9. disappears, grows over time

10. rich, poverty

Test 25

1. 55 mph x 1.6 km/mi = 88 k/h
or 88 kph

2. 80 k/h x .6 = 48.0 mph

3. 24° x 2 + 30° = 78°

4. 20° x 9/5 + 32° = 36° + 32° = 68°

5. 1 US dollar = .77 euros

$$\frac{120 \text{ euros}}{1} \times \frac{1 \text{ US dollar}}{.77 \text{ euros}} =$$

$$\frac{120}{.77} \text{ US dollars} = 156 \text{ US dollars}$$

6. 1 US dollar = .77 euros

$$\frac{65 \text{ US dollars}}{1} \times \frac{.77 \text{ euros}}{1 \text{ US dollar}} = 50 \text{ euros}$$

7. 1 US dollar = 104 yen

$$\frac{25 \text{ US dollars}}{1} \times \frac{104 \text{ yen}}{1 \text{ US dollar}} =$$
2,600 yen

8. 1 US dollar = 104 yen

$$\frac{5{,}000 \text{ yen}}{1} \times \frac{1 \text{ US dollar}}{104 \text{ yen}} =$$

$$\frac{5{,}000}{104} = \$48$$

9. diligent

10. instead of leaving it all up to God, adding some diligence to your prayers and being willing to do your part in seeing your prayer answered

Test 26

1. 3 (−1) + 1 (+2) = −1   36 − 1 = 35

2. 5 (−1) + 1 (−2) + 4 (+1) = −3, 72 − 3 = 69

3. #1 (10 + 10 + 9), #2(10 + 9 + 1),
#3(10 + 8), #4(8 + 1) = 76

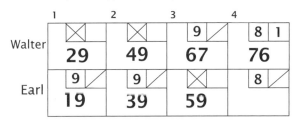

4. #1 (10+9), #2(10+10), #3(10+8+2) = 59

5. 12/29 = .414

6. A little over 2.5 since if it was 18 innings, or two full games it would be $5 \div 2 = 2.5$

   ERA $\dfrac{5 \times 9}{17} = \dfrac{45}{17} = 2.65$

7. Bjorn Borg

8. #4 and #5

9. borrower

10. As it says in Proverbs 22:7, the dynamics of your relationship have changed and your friend or relative is now your servant.

Test 27

1. 8.5 in by 11 in

2. Paper that is 8 1/2 in x 14 inches is called legal paper

3. 12 points in a pica

4. There are four 5.5" x 8.5" signatures are on a page 11" by 17". Two over and two up.

   17 in

8.5 in	8.5 in
5.5 in	5.5 in
5.5 in	5.5 in
8.5 in	8.5 in

   11 in

5. 5.5 in x 8.5 in

6. 500 sheets of paper in a ream

7. 10 reams of paper in a case

8. $2{,}750 \div 500 = 5.5$ so 6 reams

9. Collateral is something of value that is put up to the bank with the same value as the amount of the loan

10. Surety is like human collateral. This is a person co-signing on a loan guaranteeing the value of the money being borrowed. Collateral is a thing and surety is a person. Both guarantee the value of the loan.

Test 28

1.

Course	% Grade	Letter Grade	Credit Grade	Calculation
Astronomy	92	A	3	4 x 3 = 12
Algebra 2	88	B	3	3 x 3 = 9
Chemistry	86	B	3	3 x 3 = 9
US History	95	A	3	4 x 3 = 12
Latin	79	C	3	2 x 3 = 6
Drafting	90	A	2	4 x 2 = 8
			17	56 3.29

2. $56 \div 17 = 3.29$

3. All of the classes except drafting. The credits tell this, as 3 credits is 3 class hours per week.

4.

Course	% Grade	Letter Grade	Credit Grade	Calculation
Astronomy	92	A-	3	3.7 x 3 = 11.1
Algebra 2	88	B+	3	3.3 x 3 = 9.9
Chemistry	86	B	3	3 x 3 = 9
US History	95	A	3	4 x 3 = 12
Latin	79	C+	3	2.3 x 3 = 6.9
Drafting	90	A-	2	3.7 x 2 = 7.4
			17	56.3 3.31

5. $56.3 \div 17 = 3.31$

6. $1.76°$

$$WC = 91.4 - \left(.47 - .02 \times 16 + .30 \times \sqrt{16}\right)\left(91.4 - 25\right)$$
$$WC = 91.4 - \left(.47 - .02 \times 16 + .30 \times 4\right)\left(66.4\right)$$
$$WC = 91.4 - \left(.47 - .32 + 1.2\right)\left(66.4\right)$$
$$WC = 91.4 - \left(1.35\right)\left(66.4\right)$$
$$WC = 91.4 - 89.64 = 1.76°$$

7. The wind moves the warm air envelope that surrounds your body, making you feel colder than the temperature if there was no wind.

8. That he would not be a burden to those whom he was serving. (v. 9)

9. You will have money to give to those who are needy.

10. tentmaker

Test 29

1. Book your reservation at least 7 days in advance of your flight and preferably 14 or 21 days before your departure.

2. If you have several people driving, the cost of operating the car is the same as only one person making the trip.

3. The cost is usually higher (and it is a long way down).

4. less personal energy expended on the trip, as you can sleep, eat, read, or eat as someone else drives

5. American Automobile Association

6. 1,439 miles

7. 2,560 miles

8. Atlanta: 716 miles

9. In the Lord's prayer, which is instruction on how to pray, Jesus teaches us to ask God for our daily bread. We need God's blessing more than a regular salary.

10. In Deuteronomy 8:10-14 we are strongly cautioned to not forget God when we are experiencing God's blessing on our food and other material comforts.

Test 30

1. United States Postal Service

2. red, white, blue

3. UPS

4. brown

5. not usually

6. Southwest

7. west

8. 180°

9. good, perfect

10. give thanks